HYPERREALITY

BEYOND THE HORIZON WHERE PHYSICS MEETS CONSCIOUSNESS

JOHANNA BLOMQVIST

Mindstream Publishing

Helsinki, Finland, 2021

ISBN (paper): 978-952-69724-0-4

ISBN (EPUB): 978-952-69724-1-1

Cover images:

Image of Flammarion wood engraving by an unknown artist, first appeared in Camille Flammarion's L'atmosphère: météorologie populaire (1888).

Background image by Note Thanum, Unsplash

Johanna's photo: Julia Alakulju

HYPERREALITY

Contents

PREFACE ____ i

INTRODUCTION WHY IS UNDERSTANDING REALITY IMPORTANT? ____ 1

CHAPTER 1 ABOUT METAPHYSICS ____ 7

About the essence of being ____ 7

Whose reality? ____ 10

About metaphysics and the importance of philosophical discussions ____ 11

CHAPTER 2 ARE WE ONLY MACHINES? ____ 14

Mind-body problem ____ 14

Matter is the basis of everything? ____ 22

Is panpsychism the answer to problems of materialism? ____ 26

Is it time to let go of materialism? ____ 28

CHAPTER 3 CAN WE UNDERSTAND THE ESSENCE OF REALITY? 32

Plato and what REALLY IS ____ 32

Mind is more fundamental than matter? ____ 37

The confrontation of materialism and idealism ____ 39

Are we not supposed to understand the essence of reality? ____ 40

CHAPTER 4 WHAT IS THE CONNECTION BETWEEN CONSCIOUSNESS AND REALITY? ____ 43

What does consciousness mean? ____ 43

Is consciousness born in the brain? ____ 47

Matter is consciousness ____ 51

Consciousness is collective? 55
Consciousness = Qi 58
Consciousness and experimentalism 62
CHAPTER 5 OBSERVATION AFFECTS REALITY? 66
Consciousness collapses the wave of possibilities? 66
Does quantum physics describe the true reality? 75
From objectivity to subjectivity 77
CHAPTER 6 QUANTUM REALITY 81
We are one 82
Reality fades when described accurately 85
Reality is irrational 86
Reality is entangled 87
There is a mental side to reality 89
CHAPTER 7 CAN WE AFFECT PHYSICAL REALITY? 92
Human-machine interaction 93
Psychokinesis 97
Remote influencing in living systems 100
Space is a creation? 103
CHAPTER 8 DO WE HAVE FREE WILL? 105
According to classical physics, everything is already decided 106
Quantum physics makes free will possible 107
What do experiments tell us about free will? 108
Can information travel to the past? 109
It is and it isn't 110
CHAPTER 9 COINCIDENCE OR SYNCHRONICITY? 112

Synced in time 112
Explanation for synchronicity 115
CHAPTER 10 IS TIME ONLY AN ILLUSION? 118
What is time? 119
There is no time at all? 120
About the direction of time 124
Retrocausality 125
Time is a byproduct 131
CHAPTER 11 QUANTIZED SPACE-TIME 133
What is the theory of everything? 133
Is string theory the solution? 135
Dark matter and dark energy? 141
Where is consciousness? 145
CHAPTER 12 CHANGING WORLDVIEW 149
Spiritual reality 151
A model merging science and spirituality 155
The manifesto 158
CHAPTER 13 REALITY IS... 162
CHAPTER 14 REALITY IS... A SIMULATION 164
Simulated reality? 164
Is reality a simulation created by consciousness? 166
Answers to questions 169
CHAPTER 15 LIVING IN HYPERREALITY 174
Principle of consciousness 174
Principle of oneness 175

Principle of interaction 176
Principle of complementarity 176
Principle of freedom 177
Instructions 177
EPILOGUE 179
GLOSSARY 181
ACKNOWLEDGMENTS 183
REFERENCES 185
ABOUT THE BOOK AND AUTHOR 195

PREFACE

I'd like to know what this whole show is all about before it's out.

—Physicist John A. Wheeler, *Geons, Black Holes & Quantum Foam*

I realized when I was three or four years old: My mother doesn't know my thoughts. She doesn't know what I know and she doesn't feel or experience what I do. We are separated and I am an individual. We are not one.

I remember realizing this was a huge shock for me. My whole worldview fell to pieces. I felt that I was alone. There I was, and then there were others, and we weren't the same, one. Instead, we could even be against each other! I was lying in the snow screaming and kicking, since we didn't go to the supermarket to get the teddy bear I desperately wanted.

Gradually, I naturally learned to accept that I am a separate being. I figured in my mind that everything would become clearer for me later. I thought adults knew the purpose of everything and the reason why we live and are here. I also thought that as I grew a little bit older, understanding of all of this would open up for me as well.

Then I became familiar with the children's book called *The World Around Us*, and I was no longer sure if I would be able to find answers. The book began with a story of three scholars meeting the king and queen to present their view of the world:

The first scholar describes how his conception is similar to the old Egyptian conception of the world: The world is a large room with earth and seas forming the floor, and the sky supported by pillars. The stars and the moon are lanterns that light up in the evenings. The other scholar, instead, describes how his view is similar to the old Indian concept: the earth is shaped like a bow, and elephants carry it on their backs. As the elephants move, there will be earthquakes. Elephants stand on top of a giant turtle and a turtle on a giant cobra. The king and queen fell in love with these thoughts.

The last scholar said that his thoughts were the newest: According to him, the earth is a ball on which people walk. At the bottom of the ball, people walk like flies on the ceiling and, on the sides, poke out of the ball's surface. The king and queen kicked the scholar out of their castle, thinking his thoughts crazy!

The book was written from a very Western perspective, and its view hardly attached any value to the Eastern traditions of wisdom. However, as a child, I liked the book because it was about the issues of life, the world, and reality that I was concerned with. To my shock, I also realized that adults did not seem to have a common understanding of the world, reality and our purpose here. Perceptions change and have changed over time, and we still don't even agree. So, apparently, there was no Book of Life explaining all the secrets. I had thought that when I went to school, the knowledge of this book would be revealed to me. My worldview was in crisis again. At the age of about 10, I pondered existence, reality, and the question of life and death.

So it shouldn't be surprising that I later went to university to study physics, still driven to find answers to questions I had as a kid. I was hoping that in physics, there might be a theory that would perfectly explain reality. The desire to understand the world, reality and the purpose of everything has also taken me to the frontiers of science and to topics physicists do not often approach. In my book *From Quantum Physics to Energy Healing – A Physicist's Journey to Mind and Healing*, I approached one of the topics that has changed my worldview – energy healing. With energy healing, I also encountered a confrontation between science and spirituality. Can a university-trained scientist do energy healing or even address such a topic? Isn't the whole subject a hoax? In many cases, the topic of the question alone can be so sensitive that it is already excluded from scientific thinking and viewed as inappropriate; scientists even avoid entertaining it, fearing a backlash of opinions based on prevailing thinking. It seems that humankind hasn't learned anything during hundreds of years. Thoughts that differ from the prevailing thinking are mocked and excluded in the same way now as during the times of Galileo Galilei and many others. What is unknown or perceived as a threat is kicked out like the third scholar in the children's story. However, in my view, it is the physicist's job to approach any subject openly, but with the scholar's attitude of critical thinking and seeking answers. By trying to understand what we are experiencing, we constantly learn more about ourselves and the world.

One of the conclusions of my previous book was that science does not conflict with energy healing. Similarities can be sought in the world of quantum physics: Could this phenomenon be the same as those? However, one cannot draw direct conclusions from quantum physics to energy healing, since quantum physics was created to represent only the material world. Energy healing is a phenomenon that cannot be explained with our current prevailing materialistic worldview, which is the one on which physics is built. We need to expand our thinking and look for a new model to explain it. However, many of the studies I familiarized myself with and my own experiences didn't allow me to reject the subject.

There is a lot in the world that we don't yet understand. The scientific worldview is incomplete. There are even phenomena that have arisen from the scientific community that haven't been or still cannot be explained. The mind and consciousness are involved in many of these phenomena. Even in science, there is a growing realization that it is almost impossible to construct a research system separate from the observer, and the observer always has significance.

There have been tremendous upheavals in physics in the 20th century that are still ongoing. In fact, the upheavals have been so huge that there are dozens of different interpretations of the meaning of quantum physics. The materialistic-reductionist worldview that prevails in Western society still adheres to "old" physics, that is, Newton's classical model from the 17th century, even though modern physics has already advanced beyond that. The development of Western society, with its technologies, is largely due to inventions in physics, but our thinking still lags behind.

So I am diving into the topic that has been of interest to me since childhood: What is reality? Could modern physics help us to understand? What kind of worldview does it really shape for us? Could science and spirituality be united into one worldview that stems from modern physics?

As a physicist, I naturally approach the topic of reality from the perspective of physics and especially through modern physics. Modern physics has made leaps and bounds, especially in the last century. However, the question of reality needs to be approached a little more broadly, since modern science is only about 400 years old. Even physics may not have the right or entire answer.

My own view of reality is based on modern physics, research done on the frontiers of science, Western education, and familiarity with Eastern philosophies and history. A lot of interesting research has also been done recently on issues such as consciousness, including hypotheses that could open up a new understanding on the topic.

You can read this book from beginning to end, or you can first read those chapters that intrigue you based on your own interest. However, read the Epilogue last. I intentionally return to the same topics repeatedly in the book, bringing new insights that I have learned during the journey. Understanding reality is not straightforward. It is about learning to know ourselves, and we need to return to the same topics over and over again in different contexts – thus perceiving reality from many different angles.

I hope you enjoy the book. I wrote it for readers who have been thinking about the nature of reality, consciousness and the connection between science and spirituality. It is also meant for you who are feeling lost and may be thinking about the purpose of everything and your place.

This book is the answer I wanted to find as a teen, when I was contemplating the question of reality, why I am here, and how I should live. I would also think of giving this book to my own children and to my godchildren if they ever wonder about the same questions.

Johanna Blomqvist

Helsinki, April 2021

INTRODUCTION
WHY IS UNDERSTANDING REALITY IMPORTANT?

You see what you are ready to see.

Have you ever wondered why we are here and what "reality" is?

These days, questions like this are not often asked, at least not in the media or in other public contexts. In fact, you may not consider them to be important at all. Perhaps you think science should be able to provide answers.

Today, there are different explanations of reality – based on various political ideologies, scientific theories, religious doctrines and other approaches – but very few people can find their purpose and meaning in life from those. The situation today is very different from, say, the early 17th century, when the church had a great deal of control over people's lives and thinking. Our prevailing worldview today is characterized by scientific materialism, according to which we are only biological machines made of meat with no deeper purpose. This outlook on the world has its consequences: In today's society, whereas there is more prosperity in the world, albeit unevenly distributed, we may experience more alienation and loneliness than ever before. People are seeking their own place and value in the world, and are also wondering about the purpose of everything. Many are unhappy and lost. And the impact of egoistic thinking on the state of our planet is almost too obvious to mention.

Although our prevailing thinking is materialistic, very few of us feel personally that our thinking is based on the materialistic worldview of reality. One's worldview is also shaped by what one believes and emphasizes as important values or ways to influence others in one's life. You might be an agnostic, an environmental activist, a religious fundamentalist, a climate change denier, a political activist, a free thinker, a spiritual person, or a skeptic. However, a materialistic-reductionist view of the world underlies our Western society and influences our thinking, including our underlying assumptions about what reality is. We have unknowingly adopted its ideas.

Worldview and the concept of *reality* are often considered as synonyms, but they are not completely alike. A worldview contains beliefs and attitudes and shapes our behavior. The concept of reality is a more fundamental understanding of what we are experiencing. In this book, I am especially interested in that.

The concept of reality is the basis for our worldview. It is fundamental to all of our thoughts, beliefs and values, based on which each of us perceives ourselves and our place in this world: *Who am I? What is my purpose?* The concept of reality basically determines what kind of approach we have to life – whether our life has a direction, and whether we feel that life has a purpose. Although we are usually unaware of it, the concept of reality affects us all. The concept we gradually adopt as we grow or which we choose determines how we look at reality, what we notice, and even what kind of questions we are able to ask and how we seek answers to those. It is the lens through which we see the world. Through rose-colored glasses, the world looks different than it would through dark sunglasses. Inquiring into the concept of reality and pondering the worldview constructed based on that is not only for philosophers but is an important challenge for each one of us. Are we able to identify the types of glasses we wear, change the glasses, or even identify where the glasses came from?

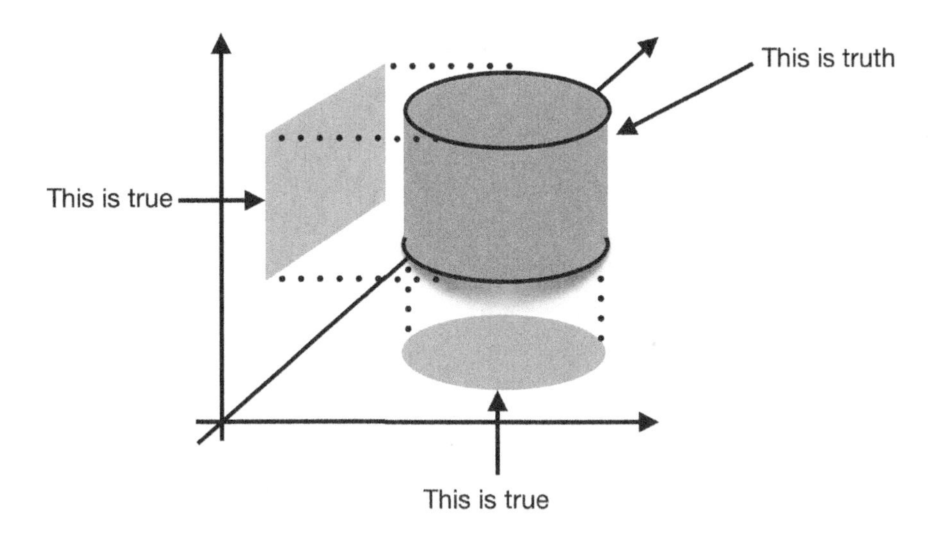

FIGURE 1. A CYLINDER THAT LOOKS LIKE A CIRCLE FROM ONE DIRECTION AND A RECTANGLE OR A SQUARE FROM ANOTHER DIRECTION.

The worldview, in addition to guiding what we usually observe and notice in our daily lives, also guides our choices, and even the values we live by. Very roughly, as in Figure 1, if we look at the cylinder from above, we see a circle, if from the side, we see a rectangle or a square. Both are true, but we see only one side – one aspect – of reality. The primary, "true" reality may even be something else.

Physicist Sir Arthur Eddington states that 99 out of 100 people have not really thought about what it means to "exist" or how to define something as "real." We in the Western world rely on scientific realism, that is, on the assumption that scientific theories are true descriptions of reality and that we can trust them. However, our scientific theories are merely models of reality, not unchanging or perfect descriptions. We've seen the models change throughout the ages, but each era seems to assume that the prevailing knowledge is correct and true. Examples can be found throughout history.

HEARTBEATS

One example of how a worldview guides our thinking is the discovery of the heartbeat at around 1618 by William Harvey, the doctor of the King of England. Harvey didn't agree with the prevailing view of human physiology, which was still based on the ideas of Aristotle, Galen, Celsus, and some other learned men from antiquity. According to this older model, the function of the heart was to act as a heater that warmed the blood that had cooled in the brain due to its functioning. The blood circulation was therefore due to heat movement, and the heart's duties didn't involve pumping blood.

However, when Harvey examined dogs, he discovered that the heart was really moving and pumping blood. He thus redefined the function of the heart as a pump that sends blood into the circulatory system while producing a special sound, heartbeats, that can be detected. When Harvey published his findings, the whole of Europe resisted. Emilio Parisano of Venice, one of the experts of medicine and philosophy of the time, wrote: "*There is no one in Venice who hears a heartbeat.*"

The heart was known to beat; of course people had noticed the heartbeats of their own body, or noticed, for example, how the beat could change. However, as a phenomenon it didn't exist, so there was no theory to describe it.

The worldview and concomitant assumptions influence our expectations and what we experience, thus limiting our perception of different phenomena. What does not exist in our conception of reality and the theories that underpin it, we usually do not notice; or we ignore it or consider it impossible, unless we have intentionally broken with our assumptions and sought new perspectives and, for at least a moment, abandoned the prevailing way of thinking.

From time to time, there have been upheavals in history in which the entire prevailing way of thinking has been found deficient, or flat-out wrong. In science, such disruptions have occurred almost regularly. One of the biggest upheavals that has touched both science and religion was probably the shift from a geocentric to a heliocentric solar system model. The life of the average person has probably been more affected by changes in medical theories and the treatments for disease which result from them. In the 1540s, an anatomy book by Andreas Vesalius, *De humani corporis fabrica libri septem*, replaced the former authority, the 1,300-year-old model of Galen, which was based on animal autopsies, because in the time of Galen, around 130 BC, human dissection was forbidden. One of the most significant medical changes occurred in the late 19th century with the discovery of bacteria by Louis Pasteur, which led to the germ theory of disease and vaccination.

At this moment in history, we are going through a time of change as our worldview adjusts to new discoveries. At the beginning of the 20th century, quantum physics brought with it revolutionary ideas that challenged the prevailing, materialistic worldview's ability to accurately describe the world, and modern physics has already progressed far beyond that. A change began, which is still unfolding in our world. This change in the model has already led to technological advances and to our lives changing tremendously, but there is an even greater shift in thinking going on.

The task of science – and especially of physics – is often given as studying the basic laws common to all natural phenomena. Discovering "the basic law" implies seeking both mathematical precision and a deeper understanding to find a common explanation. The essence, therefore, is to ascertain what reality is, though this is often considered a matter of metaphysics. So, inevitably, to approach the question of what reality is, I have to enter into philosophical reflection and metaphysics (Chapter 1), which is perhaps atypical for a physicist, and approach the subject from outside modern science. Modern science is about 400 years old, which is a short time in the history of humankind. However, there are other approaches to the question, such as documented cases and historical information throughout recorded history, that can help us better understand reality. Already in Ancient Greece, Plato wrote about the nature of reality, and other literature from antiquity discusses the concept of reality. All of these together can help us to understand what reality really is.

In Chapter 2, "Are we just machines?", I consider the view of reality the current materialistic model forms for us, where it comes from and what it means to us. In Chapters 3 and 4, I seek to answer the question of whether it is ever truly possible for us to understand what reality is, and I explore the relation between consciousness and reality. These issues have been pondered for thousands of years, and I certainly cannot do justice to all of these considerations in this book, but I want to highlight the most important ones and those that have made the most sense to me.

My own thinking has changed a lot in recent years, in part because I have become acquainted with research being done on the frontiers of science. When I was doing my PhD in physics in 2001, I thought I understood the physics behind everything, how the world was constructed and how it functions. Over the past 10 years, I have explored topics that I may have ignored earlier. Such topics include spirituality, consciousness, mind and subtle energy (*qi*). These are not dealt with in physics studies, and in fact the whole living being is not included in physics studies. Medical physics and biophysics, of course, deal with the human, but not these subjects. However, even in physics, the human – the observer, the experimenter – plays a key role (Chapter 5). The role of human consciousness must be understood so that we can also understand the results of scientific research. No science is really objective, as you will learn in Chapters 5 to 7.

Perhaps inquiring into free will (Chapter 8) and understanding the nature of time and synchronicity (Chapters 9 and 10) could open the question of reality. Perhaps the answer to understanding reality is the theory of everything that has been dreamed of in physics for decades (Chapter 11). One topic that is often overlooked in the books of physicists dealing with reality is spirituality, but in order to fully understand reality, we must also seek understanding by avenues other than reason – through the irrational, metaphysical, phenomenological paths of inquiry. I wonder if science and spirituality could be placed in the same worldview (Chapter 12). How would reality be explained and what would such a reality really mean to us (Chapters 13–15)?

CHAPTER 1
ABOUT METAPHYSICS

Metaphysics means nothing but an unusually obstinate effort to think clearly.

—William James

That's metaphysics, my dear fellow! It's forbidden me by my doctor, my stomach won't take it.

—Boris Pasternak

What do I mean by "reality"? When I talk about reality in this book, I mean everything that is true, real and existing, that is, the state of existence as things really are, and what kind of laws govern them. Physically speaking, reality can be thought of as meaning everything that comprises the universe, everything that is already known and still unknown. This is how reality is often described in Western culture. I'm looking for an answer to the question of what really IS.

This question about reality is a metaphysical one. What does this mean? Some things we can objectively measure, but when we seek an answer to the question of what reality is, we also have to take into account the assumptions behind it. What are the assumptions, what is the worldview, on which our reflections or research are based? This is where we enter the realm of metaphysics, and where we pose questions at the threshold between science and philosophy.

About the essence of being

The word *metaphysics* comes from the root words *meta* and *physika* (in Greek *ta meta ta physika*), meaning "*after physics.*" The term dates back to the writings of Greek philosopher Aristotle which, when they were compiled, included texts on the nature of reality in a section *after* the texts on physics. The name for these texts, metaphysics, gradually became the name for the whole topic. Metaphysics is, in fact, a continuation of physics: both try to understand what the world – reality – really is. Instead of concentrating on what can be observed, metaphysics seeks to understand what underlies the laws of nature. Metaphysics is a search for the most basic *being* (Latin *Ens inquantum ens*). Ontology may be considered a part of metaphysics, as it is the study of being, becoming, and existence: what it means to exist and what exists.

Science journalist Aaron Neil explains the difference between science and metaphysics (Aaron Neil, *Quillette*, May 8, 2019):

> Science is a method used to discover facts about the material world. Metaphysics, instead, deals with the whole of reality, or put in philosophical language, being as such. Where science discloses the properties of the physical world, metaphysics ventures beyond the physical and explores the fundamental nature of all that is.

Metaphysics as a scientific-philosophical domain has gone through shifts in cultural meaning over the millennia. It can be divided into two broad ideological-historical phases: classical Aristotelian metaphysics was coupled with the study of the natural world – which we call "physics" and was referred to for centuries as "natural philosophy." Then, after the scientific revolution of the 17th century, metaphysics and the study of nature by observation were divided into separate arenas: philosophy and empirical science. The basis of these phases was different. The aim of the Aristotelian approach was to understand the unchanging structure of reality, the fundamental nature of being, the first causes. Aristotle states in his *Metaphysics*:

> Everyone takes what is called 'wisdom' (*sophia*) to be concerned with the primary causes (*aitia*) and the starting-points (or principles, *archai*).

He also states in *Metaphysics*:

> ALL men by nature desire to know. An indication of this is the delight we take in our senses; for even apart from their usefulness they are loved for themselves; and above all others the sense of sight. For not only with a view to action, but even when we are not going to do anything, we prefer seeing (one might say) to everything else. The reason is that this, most of all the senses, makes us know and brings to light many differences between things.

In Aristotelian metaphysics it is assumed that there is an external world that is independent of the consciousness of its observer, and it is in our interest to study the causes and principles behind everything. The goal of the new empirical science, a quantitative model based on observation and experiment, was to exploit the natural order for the benefit of man. Its purpose could be said to be instrumental rather than philosophical. Nature is described by theories and mathematics derived from observation, and it can be understood through experiments that elucidate natural laws. Until the beginning of the scientific era, metaphysics had been the basis of everything, but now there was less interest in the goal of understanding the reality behind the scientific approach. There were attempts to reform metaphysics to better align with the new scientific endeavor, but not with very good results. Eventually, by the 19th century and the predominance of positivism, metaphysics was rejected almost completely as an aspect of the modern scientific worldview.

During the 20th century, however, perhaps due in part to the development of modern physics and the ideas, thoughts, and understanding it brought with it, metaphysics returned to the scene along with the quest to find more common, fundamental laws. The attempt to unite all the interactions of physics and form a theory of everything is an example of this return of metaphysics. Discussions are going on now about time, space, free will, and our role in all this in different contexts in which science and philosophy are once more overlapping. We are discovering again that metaphysical thinking is an essential part of humanity – we have a need to try to understand reality, as Aristotle stated.

Whose reality?

If I had never seen a giraffe or even heard of its existence, it would not be part of my reality. For someone else, it would be a reality, true and existing. There are things that are reality for one and not for another. Even in the realm of science, there are many theories, parts of theories, or hypotheses that are a reality for one and not considered possible by others at all. I will talk about many of these in this book. One such topic is the question of consciousness: Is it the creator of everything or a product of the brain? Another example is the assumption of the existence of dark matter – the name itself originates in our not knowing what it is.

What is true and who defines it? Usually, the view of reality is collectively determined by the majority. Often, this collective view of reality is so automatic that we don't even question our beliefs or even see them as beliefs, as if this knowledge is given. We think that life will end when we die, if we have been raised to believe in this kind of model of life. Nowadays, it is common for truth to be determined by a scientific view that is thought to be objective. The view of reality given by physics, the foundation of science, is considered to be all-encompassing and correct because it is based on empirical research and data. Physics describes all phenomena – from that seen through the microscope, including small particles and atoms, to everyday phenomena familiar to us, all the way to the cosmic phenomena of stars, galaxies, and the entire universe. Science is often placed in the position that for millennia was held by God: It is supposed to be all seeing and reveal what the real truth is. Scientists now hold the keys to the truth once held by the church.

However, what is true and what is real are not the same thing.

We all have our own realities, and they have commonalities and differences. I can't say that my reality would be more true than someone else's. Even the view of science cannot be considered the same as the truth (see Figure 1 in the Introduction). We all see reality through our own glasses, but together we may have a better understanding of the whole. That is why, in this book, I also talk about approaches to the question of reality that are not in line with the prevailing paradigm, that is, what is established and often considered correct thinking.

About metaphysics and the importance of philosophical discussions

I am a physicist, and I would like to justify why I see metaphysics and philosophical debate as important, as there are also scientists and scholars who consider these to be secondary and don't see the need to consider philosophy in any way. Even physicist Stephen Hawking stated in his 2011 conference address that "philosophy is dead." According to him, philosophy has not kept pace with the development of physics, and physics has usurped the role of philosophy, as it is able to explain the fundamental questions of the universe. However, not everyone agrees. According to physicist Carlo Rovelli, such thinking has been typical particularly since the second half of the 20th century. Perhaps this is due to the large number of applications of quantum physics, which were developed without philosophical thinking, that is, without truly considering what quantum physics means. In *The Order of Time,* Rovelli states:

> Heisenberg would never have contributed to the birth of quantum mechanics if he had not had a full understanding of philosophy. Einstein would not have brought about the theory of relativity without reading the ideas of philosophers, and Galileo would never have made his inventions without understanding Plato. Newton considered himself a philosopher and began by becoming acquainted with Descartes' philosophical ideas.

Einstein states in his 1936 article on physics and reality that as long as science is in a state of change, and there are phenomena that cannot be explained by prevailing theories, scientists should also consider their work from a philosophical perspective – what their study results really mean. Only in a situation where one can rely on the prevailing paradigm to describe the world correctly would philosophizing be less necessary – if ever. Such a situation did not yet exist when Einstein died in 1955, and the situation has not changed substantially in the last 60-plus years.

Scientific research involves certain processes and methods, including observation, hypothesis, experiments, data collection, analysis of results, and so on. Every scientist has a certain worldview of his or her own, an understanding of reality that is not limited to space, time, or matter, but also includes life, mind, behavior, society, history, and so on. Everything happens in our own worldview, which also guides the direction of research, what is sought, and even what is seen. Something essential can go unnoticed if you close your eyes to the essentials. This is illustrated in a YouTube video I saw recently: Everyone is asked to count how many times a basketball changes hands during the video. Up to 40% of viewers don't notice a gorilla dancing in the video because they focus so completely on counting!

The mentality of "shut up and calculate" has deep roots in science. The phrase comes from David Merman, a physicist and professor emeritus at Cornell University, who wanted to sum up what the most famous interpretation of quantum physics, the Copenhagen interpretation, means to him and many other physicists. Does the physicist need to consider the philosophy behind the calculations? Many physicists think that the philosophy of science should be left to philosophers and that physicists need not consider what the results actually suggest. Part of the problem is that such pondering is hardly taught in school or university. Studying the philosophy of science, for example, in university physics studies, is often dependent only on an individual student's interest. Even scholars often forget that science is based in philosophy. Science is connected to understanding reality. The worldviews and different perceptions of reality should be taught early in school, for example under the subject of Skills of Living.

Philosopher Bernardo Kastrup states in his book *Dreamed Up Reality*: *"If you never ask yourself a philosophical question, you will leave behind an unexplored life."*

Therefore, my question is: What is reality? Are we just "machines," as our current prevailing materialistic-reductionistic worldview suggests?

CHAPTER 2
ARE WE ONLY MACHINES?

Life is but a motion of limbs.

—Thomas Hobbes (1588–1679)

I believe that there is a fundamental mystery in my existence, transcending any biological account of the development of my body (including my brain) with its genetic inheritance and its evolutionary origin. ...I cannot believe that this wonderful gift of a conscious existence has no further future, no possibility of another existence under some other unimaginable conditions.

—Sir John Carew Eccles (Australian neurophysiologist and Nobel Prize winner in Physiology or Medicine 1963, *Facing Reality: Philosophical Adventures by a Brain Scientist*, 1970)

The question of whether we are just machines includes the question of our purpose, as well as what happens when we die. Our lives are dominated by a worldview where the soul has no place. We live isolated and in a world of ego and self-centeredness. Our world is out of balance. How has this come about?

Mind-body problem

To understand the current prevailing view of reality, one must go all the way back to the 16th and 17th centuries, a time which is often described as the beginning of a new era – the Renaissance. During this period in Western culture, the intellectual, artistic, and spiritual atmosphere opened up to different views, and the knowledge-seeking gaze shifted from God to man.

Developments in science eroded the prestige and authority of the Church. Nicolaus Copernicus, Johannes Kepler, and Galileo Galilei showed that the earth-centered model of the universe was erroneous. This era is often referred to as the dawn of an era of reason, empiricism, and experimental science. However, the change did not take place easily, for this was also the period of the Inquisition, the Church's means to control the beliefs of the populace. "Heretics" were punished for believing in things that brought the authority of the Church into doubt. And as we know, Galileo was sentenced by the Inquisition in 1633 to imprisonment for blasphemy and eventually to house arrest for the rest of his life because of his thoughts. It was not until 1992, that the Vatican formally admitted its mistake in condemning Galileo.

However, the proofs of empirical science could not be denied forever, and as the 17th century went on, the mechanical, materialistic worldview took hold, and the soul, or mind, was left out of consideration. Galileo and other scientists and philosophers who initiated the development of modern science, such as Sir Isaac Newton and René Descartes, among others, were not atheists but Christians. Their view of the world was dualistic, and in it God was separate from nature, and nature was the way to truth. Descartes describes in his lesser-known work *The Search for Truth by the Light of Nature* the study of nature as:

> The search for truth by the light of nature, entirely pure and without the aid of religion or philosophy, determines what ideas an honest person should have of anything he may think about; it penetrates to the most fascinating secrets of the sciences. (Author's translation from original French.)

There were, in a way, two different worlds: the material world and the immaterial, or intangible, world of spirits, which included God, angels, spirits, and the human mind. The view is often referred to as Cartesian dualism, or the "mind-body divide."

Until the Renaissance, a holistic picture of the world and man had prevailed, and the world was seen as a living entity. Soon, though, the view changed. God had created the world, but after its creation it functioned like an automatic machine. In this new view, there was less and less room for the intangible, such as the soul, spirit, or consciousness.

In his *Meditations on First Philosophy* (1641), Descartes did not describe man, but a kind of conceptual model of man, namely creatures created by God, which consist of two ingredients, a body and a soul:

> These men will be composed, as we are, of a soul and a body. First I must describe the body on its own; then the soul, again on its own; and finally I must show how these two natures would have to be joined and united in order to constitute men who resemble us.

Unfortunately, Descartes did not fulfill all of his promises: he discussed only the body and said almost nothing about the soul and its interaction with the body.

Descartes' contemporary, mathematician and philosopher Thomas Hobbes, even went so far in his defense of this physicalism, in his book *Leviathan*, as to depict all humans and animals as machines of mere flesh and blood. Hobbes saw the world as a deterministic whole, where everything, even our own decisions, is predetermined and obeys the laws of nature. However, determinism, he said, was not in conflict with free will, as both are bound by the same laws.

According to Hobbes, the world can be reduced to the movement of physical bodies, and this model can be used to explain everything in the universe. The purpose of scientific research was to develop a description of the movement of the bodies, which will, at most, reveal causality – the cause-and-effect relationship – and ultimately the regularity of nature. He considered it self-evident that science would find an answer to questions about the nature of reality. However, even though Hobbes's view was that nature is physical, he didn't argue that we could reach everything; for example, he described the phenomenon he called "spirits," which are outside our ability to perceive, even though they do occur in the physical world. Hobbes also used the concept of spirits in trying to understand God and angels. According to Hobbes, with our incomplete comprehension, we are incapable of understanding these. For man, the information that God exists and is the creator of everything, and thus, the first cause from which everything originated, is sufficient. Hobbes's theory of humans as mere physical beings, machines, does not provide an answer to how the spiritual dimension of man can be described. Hobbes finds everything in the universe physical, but he could very well have stated that everything is immaterial spirit. In keeping with the prevailing thinking typical for that era, he leaned more strongly on physicalism.

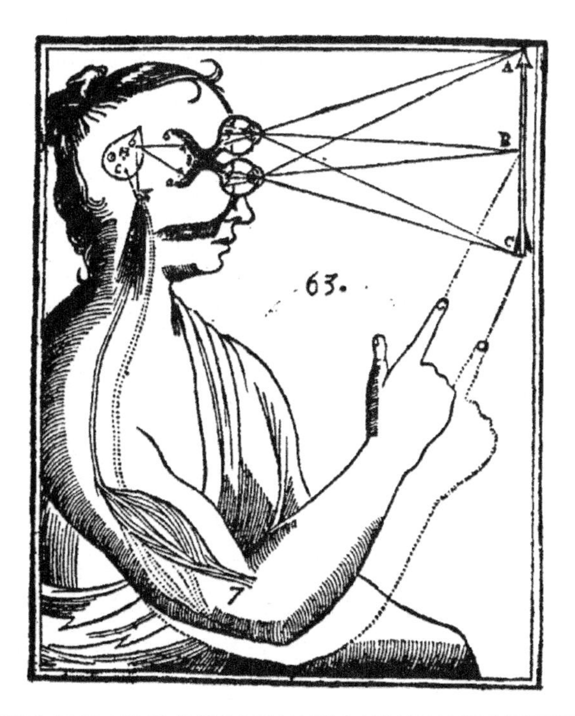

FIGURE 2. DESCARTES AND MIND-BODY DUALISM. WHAT WE EXPERIENCE IS PASSED ON BY THE SENSORY ORGANS TO THE PINEAL GLAND AND FROM THERE TO THE IMMATERIAL MIND. (WIKIMEDIA COMMONS)

The views of Hobbes and Descartes were strongly influenced by the ideas of the Renaissance, when people had become increasingly skeptical of the science of that time and the possibilities of genuine knowledge. Descartes wanted to restore the status of science, and defending a mechanistic view of reality was part of this. He defended his view of the true separation of mind and body. He regarded the pineal gland as the home of the soul and also as the connecting link between body and mind. He believed that what was experienced was transmitted through the senses to the pineal gland and from there to the immaterial mind (Figure 2). According to current knowledge, the pineal gland produces and regulates some hormones, such as melatonin levels, that are linked to sleep rhythm. It also has a connection to the regulation of emotions. The pineal gland has played a significant role in many ancient cultures and is still often referred to as "the third eye" today. It is interesting, therefore, that the pineal gland has pin and rod cells and vitreous fluid that sense light similar to those in the eye. The pineal gland also has a connection to the visual cortex.

Based on magnetic resonance imaging (MRI) devices, we know that what we experience has a connection with brain functioning. However, we are unable to explain how experiences are transferred to our minds, that is, what the link is between the material and the immaterial world.

The mind-body problem could be briefly summed up, in the eyes of the dualist, in the question: How is it possible that the body and the mind can interact with each other when one is material in nature and the other immaterial?

According to Descartes, the figurehead of mind-body dualism, our body is a complex clockwork with a mysterious link to the immaterial mind. The only thing we can't explain is how we have the ability to have an intellectual conversation with each other. We still can't explain this even today.

The scientific approach to the mind-body problem is to use observation and collect data: one can study what happens in a person's brain and body as they have certain experiences and go through different states of consciousness. These data might be about behavior or the display of neural activity in an fMRI scan. Such studies provide data on what is happening in another person's mind (i.e., third-person data). Even more challenging to study is the so-called first-person problem, that is, what happens in our own minds. In order for it to be studied by scientific means, first-person data should be treated as if it were third-person data, that is, objectively. Indeed, the ultimate challenge of studying the mind-body problem through science is to connect what we feel and experience in our own minds with what we observe to happen in the mind of another.

The mind-body problem could also be described through our personal experience: I have a body, but where am *I*? There is activity of mind, consciousness and also dreams. Are these all the same thing? This seems to be the case, as the body reflects the sensations of the mind, and vice versa. And can they be separate from each other? For centuries, even thousands of years, these things have been discussed. Aristotle said:

> It is the possession of a soul that makes an organism an organism at all. Soul is the form of any living thing. The soul is the first actuality of a natural body, material form, that is potentially alive.

Plato went even further:

> This essence (soul) is an incorporeal, eternal occupant of our being. Even after death, the soul exists.

The thoughts of Aristotle and Plato represented an idealistic perspective on the mind-body problem, where the mind – or the soul – is held to be more fundamental than matter.

Materialism, instead, considers matter to be more fundamental, and holds that phenomena such as God and angels are not real. There is only the human mind and that is the result of brain activity. Materialism began to gain support especially in the late 19th century, for political reasons, among others. Many scholars of that time abandoned dualism and strongly supported ontological monism. Reality was seen to consist of only one substance, which was matter, to which everything could be returned. As the authority of the Church eroded, at the same time, there were enormous breakthroughs in science, and it was easy to accept the materialist notion that only physical things exist.

Descartes practiced meditation. In his method, the meditator first ignores all his beliefs, the veracity of which can be in the slightest doubt. He subjected his beliefs to strict skeptical arguments, and asked how we can be sure of anything. Can our world be a mere illusion? The senses cannot be trusted, for they have sometimes deceived us all, as in the optical illusion of Figure 3. The horizontal lines in the image do not appear to be parallel to each other, but appear skewed, although this is not the case: The illusion is created in the brain. Nothing should be taken as given or true, but in order to obtain information, all preconceptions must be rejected.

FIGURE. 3. OPTICAL ILLUSION. THE HORIZONTAL LINES DO NOT SEEM TO BE PARALLEL, THOUGH THEY ARE.

Descartes thought it possible that everything is just a dream. When we are asleep, we hold what we experience to be true until we wake up and know we have dreamed. In a dream we do not know we are sleeping. Only in the lucid dream, in the state on the border between sleep and wakefulness, is it possible to realize that one is sleeping during a dream.

How can we be sure of anything at all when we can't even be sure if we are awake or asleep? Maybe God created us as prone to erroneous reasoning? Or perhaps there is no God, in which case we are even more likely to be imperfect, coincidental beings who are certainly constantly mistaken.

Descartes is most famous for the statement: "Cogito ergo sum. – I think, therefore I am."

In order to draw conclusions and have ideas, to think, we must exist. The skill of thinking is a sign of existence; thinking must have a source. In a way, this is in contradiction with Descartes' ideas regarding dreams and the waking state, for with our thinking we can create these states as well.

Descartes never posited a final theory about the relationship between mind and body. Many philosophers, however, say that Descartes was able to summarize many theories of past philosophers and that in his works future theories are also prefigured. Descartes shaped the foundations of the modern world with his work.

The 17th century is considered a historical turning point, with the inception of the worldview of Cartesian dualism and modern science, which also marked the beginning of the dichotomy between science and religion. A division arose between matter, which was mechanical and physical in nature, and immaterial spirit or mind. Matter belonged to science and the immaterial spirit was considered a topic for religion. The development of science, and physics in particular, benefitted from this division and the materialistic model of nature. Even then, however, it was known that science is only a model and while it didn't consider mind, a place must be found for the mind and consciousness in a scientific worldview. The mind and body are not separate, but one whole. Is the mind primary with regard to matter or vice versa? This is the chicken-or-egg problem: Which gives birth to which or did they arise together? How we view the relationship between mind and matter – the mind-body problem – determines how we perceive reality.

Matter is the basis of everything?

In the Middle Ages, the world was explained by the laws of the spiritual world. During the Renaissance, the worldview was revolutionized when new mechanistic laws of nature replaced the old ones. The English physicist Isaac Newton first formulated the philosophy of this new age as a new natural science in the *Philosophiae Naturalis Principia Mathematica* in 1687. *Principia* contains the laws of motion described by Newton, which are the basis of classical mechanics, the law of gravity and the theory of planetary motions experimentally observed by Kepler. By the end of that century, Newtonian ideas were gradually accepted. Science was able to make huge leaps and progressed tremendously, which also served as a catalyst for the Reformation and, later, for the Industrial Revolution.

Newton views the material world as a mechanical system, created by God, in which the objects under consideration are modeled like billiard balls whose behavior is determined by the laws of motion (Sir Isaac Newton in The Tao of Physics):

> It seems probable to me that God in the beginning formed matter in solid, massy, hard, im-penetrable, movable particles, of such sizes and figures, and with such other properties, and in such proportion to space, as most conduced to the end for which he formed them; and that these primitive particles being solids, are incomparably harder than any porous bodies compounded of them; even so very hard, as never to wear or break in pieces; no ordinary power being able to divide what God himself made one in the first creation.

This description is summarized in the term *atomism*, an idea which was originally posited as early as Ancient Greece. Democritus, in 400 BC, and Leukippos stated that matter consists of indivisible particles. The idea was forgotten with the advent of Aristotle's natural philosophy, and it was not until the Renaissance, when the old Aristotelian model began to become obsolete and replaced with empirical physics, that atomism was rediscovered. Descartes, Galileo, and Hobbes were all supporters of atomism. Many individuals influenced the new rise of atomism. Descartes and Gassendi both published their own versions of physics. Boyle's idea was to replace the Aristotelian physics with corpuscularism, a form of atomism, and to explain reality and its changes through unchanging particles and their motion. Boyle, in *"The Skeptical Chymist: or Chymico-Physical Doubts & Paradoxes* (1661), describes how

> certain primitive and simple, or perfectly unmingled bodies; which not being made of any other bodies, or of one another, are the ingredients of which all those called perfectly mixt bodies are immediately compounded, and into which they are ultimately resolved.

Chymico here refers to the combination of alchemy and chemistry.

Atomism became part of classical physics and chemistry in the 19th century. John Dalton formulated the first actual atomic theory in the early 19th century, which described how matter is composed of atoms. There are different types of atoms, and Dalton called these elements. Each element has its own properties and its own mass, and can form chemical compounds. In chemistry, Dalton's model was soon adopted and laid the foundation for atomic theory in modern physics.

Atoms were thought to be the smallest units of matter until 1897, when J.J. Thomson discovered electrons in his cathode ray studies. Thomson found that the rays passing through the vacuum tube consisted of negatively charged particles, which he called "corpuscles," and which were later renamed electrons. The electrons were 1,800 times smaller than the smallest atom, hydrogen (H). Based on his measurements, Thomson created an atomic model to explain why atoms are neutral, and have no charge. In the Thomson model, negatively charged corpuscles swim in a positively charged atom like raisins in a bun. Thomson's "plum pudding model" was also the first atomic model based on experiments.

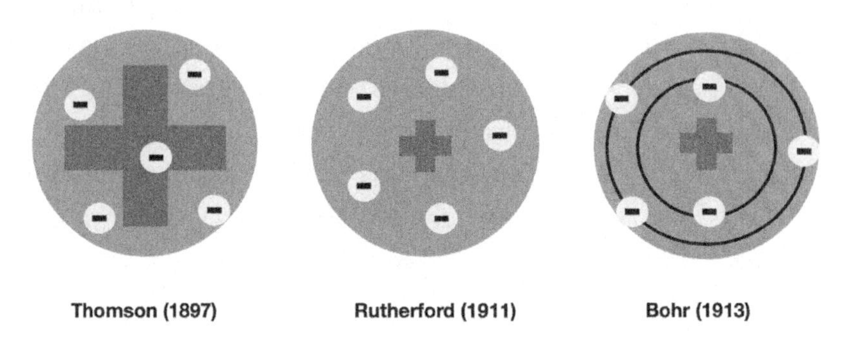

FIGURE 4. DIFFERENT MODELS FOR THE ATOM. THOMSON'S PLUM PUDDING MODE, RUTHERFORD'S MODEL AND BOHR'S MODEL FOR ATOM. ELECTRONS ARE MARKED WITH THE SYMBOL —.

Ernest Rutherford found in his experiments that the positive charge in an atom is concentrated only in a small area in the center of the atom. Therefore, he proposed a planetary model with a cloud of electrons around the positive nucleus.

Quantum theory revolutionized physics in the early 20th century and the atomic model had to be updated again. In 1900, physicist Max Planck hypothesized that electromagnetic radiation, such as light, occurs only in a certain size of energy packets, called *quanta*. In this way it was possible to explain some phenomena which could not be understood by classical, Newtonian physics. Such phenomena included photoelectric phenomena and black body radiation. Planck's description of quanta was the beginning of quantum mechanics.

Niels Bohr, one of the developers of quantum theory together with Planck, Heisenberg, and Einstein, among others, incorporated these ideas into an atomic model. In the Bohr model, electrons move around the positive core of an atom only in certain orbits according to certain rules. As they move, they simultaneously emit or absorb light at a frequency proportional to the change in energy. The understanding of atoms has since increased, for example, with the development of spectroscopy. New models are, however, difficult to describe visually. Therefore, the Bohr atomic model is still used in schools today to explain the structure of atoms. However, this is just a model that does not fully reflect reality.

Is everything, thus, basically only the motion of atoms, electrons and other particles? All matter can be broken down into smaller and smaller units and eventually always reduced to particles. Is matter, thus, the basis of everything, and perhaps all the answers to reality are to be found in particles and in their interactions? Our current prevailing materialistic-reductionistic view on reality holds matter as the basis of everything. According to it, everything can be reduced to matter and everything emerges, arises, from it. Sometimes this view is also referred to as emergent materialism, or monistic materialism. According to materialistic thinking, the basic units of matter are the atoms and elementary particles that make up all matter.

However, there are shortcomings to materialistic thinking. It works pretty well in physics and chemistry, but not so well in biology. If the world is made up of unconscious matter and is the only reality, how can we be aware? We shouldn't be. Either we are not conscious or our consciousness is not real but just the result of brain activity. If it is not real, it cannot affect the physical world, which would also mean that we do not have free will. This is how the world is seen in the current prevailing scientific thinking. But materialism cannot explain how consciousness arises.

The shortcomings of materialism lead back to the mind-body problem. Philosopher Thomas Nagel says:

> Consciousness is what makes the mind-body problem really intractable. Without consciousness the mind-body problem would be much less interesting. With consciousness it seems hopeless.

The mind and mental phenomena exist and are as real as the body. To a large extent, the mind-body problem is based on the use of causal effectiveness – the cause-effect relationship – as the measure of existence. Thus, if psychic phenomena are real and exist, they too should have the ability to affect matter.

This effectiveness is difficult to establish with current scientific means and the results can always be questioned.

There are many phenomena that we encounter almost daily, but which do not fit into the current materialistic worldview. Such phenomena are often classified as anomalies or parapsychological when it is impossible to explain them with prevailing theories. Such phenomena include premonitions, intuition, telepathy, premonition dreams, and synchronicity.

Science seeks to find objective truth, but is such a goal even possible? After all, all objective information is based on subjective observation. Robert Jahn and Brenda Dunne, founders of the PEAR (Princeton Engineering Anomalies Research) laboratory, which has studied the effect of the mind on matter for decades, say: "*Mind without matter leaves us with a world of ephemeral abstraction; matter without mind eliminates the essence of life itself.*"

Is panpsychism the answer to problems of materialism?

The biggest problem with the prevailing paradigm, then, is probably consciousness: How do mental phenomena relate to our physical reality?

According to the materialist approach, reality – that is, all the phenomena in our universe – is essentially matter. Everything can, thus, be explained as emerging from matter, including our spiritual side, psychic phenomena and consciousness. Psychic functions can be explained based on biology, biological phenomena in turn can be reduced to chemistry, and chemical processes can be reduced further to physics and ultimately to the function of elementary particles. The answer to the question of consciousness must therefore, according to this materialistic-reductionistic view, be found in elementary particles. So far, however, there has been no indication that such particles of consciousness are found in matter so as to explain where consciousness originates.

Some materialists have sought answers to the question of consciousness from panpsychism (Greek *pan,* all, *psykhē,* soul), sometimes also called panexperientialism or modern materialistic panpsychism. Panpsychism dates back to antiquity and features of it have been found in many cultures and spiritual traditions; in the East, these include Taoism, Vedanta philosophy and Mahayana Buddhism. The original panpsychism was very close to idealism. In panpsychism, it is thought that everything has consciousness to some degree, even plants and inanimate objects. Panpsychism thus shares features with animism, or even magic. Consciousness is a fundamental feature of reality in panpsychism. It is as original, or even more original, than matter and exists throughout the universe. Panpsychism as a concept encompasses a very different way of thinking about our world; on one side it begins to agree with idealism, where it is thought that there is only one mind. Many minds unite into one. On the other side, panpsychism, in turn, approaches Newtonian ideas. Many neuroscientists have begun to see panpsychism as a very possible explanatory model, such as Christof Koch, who previously relied on materialism, in his book *The Feeling of Life Itself: Why Consciousness Is Widespread but Can't Be Computed.*

The modern materialistic panpsychist thinks that consciousness is a basic property of matter. There are elements of consciousness in matter that, when combined in a body, make it conscious. In panpsychism, this is often explained by the laws of nature: Because nature follows laws, one feature of which is continuity, the non-conscious must be continuous with conscious. There cannot be a clear division between the conscious and the non-conscious.

Could elementary particles, then, have information properties? Even if they did, panpsychism is unable to explain why they would have them. It also can't explain why, as the organism becomes more complex, it should at some point become aware. These questions need to be addressed, also for example, when designing increasingly intelligent AI-based robots. Panpsychism cannot explain why this would happen, and thus does not bring the desired solution to the problem of consciousness for materialism. According to panpsychism, consciousness is fundamental, but the mind is nevertheless seen as physical in materialism. For example, philosopher Daniel Dennett has justified the physicality of the mind by saying that if the mind were non-physical in nature, it would have no physical energy or mass and thus could not affect the world. Thus, according to him, if the mind could appear from outside the physical world, this would result in the law of conservation of energy not being valid.

According to the law of conservation of energy, no energy is generated and or lost and total energy is conserved in a closed system.

The physicist Erwin Schrödinger states in his book *Mind and Matter*: *"Sensations and thoughts do not belong to the 'world of energy.' They cannot bring about change in this world."*

Maybe the situation is just as Schrödinger states. Maybe when the mind affects the physical world, it can't be considered as "energy"? Maybe the mind should be treated as quantum phenomena, the effects of which are statistical? Statistical phenomena do not change energy conservation.

If the mind were physical, then how do spiritual experiences, which we nevertheless have, arise from matter? Why do we experience these at all if matter is enough to explain everything? Matter cannot become spiritual according to the current laws of physics. If the mind is assumed to be physical, material, the problem is not yet solved.

Is it time to let go of materialism?

What if the problem is materialism itself? In our materialistic world, we can treat objects as isolated, detached, and reduce everything to individual smaller parts. Time travels linearly forward, as the clock shows. Things are predictable and manageable; the result is preceded by a cause. We have no real freedom to choose. Mind and consciousness are the product of the brain. Thus, we live in a world where we are detached and our own interests are paramount. The world of values includes greed, jealousy, pride, and other selfish, egoistic values. Our prevailing worldview has led to a world that is out of balance. The state of our planet is a testament to that.

The materialistic, Newtonian paradigm, can be summed up in the following points:

- **Causality.** According to the current understanding, our world was born in the Big Bang. The question of what was before this is impossible, for the Big Bang gave rise to all the laws and interactions of nature, including causality, that is, the cause-and-effect relationship.

- **Materialism.** Matter is the basis of everything. As a result of evolution, more and more diverse and intelligent species, such as humans, have evolved.
- **Individualism, egoism.** We are primarily individuals who act in our own interests.
- **Reductionism.** The material world can be reduced to ever smaller parts.
- **Determinism.** Everything is predetermined.
- **Evolution.** We are born as determined by our parents' genes.

We have adopted materialism unnoticed at home, at school, and elsewhere in society. However, it is time to move on from materialism, for it is just one way of perceiving the world, one kind of lens to see through, and does not seem to explain the whole reality. Our world can no longer go on in this way.

Materialism led to scientific and technological developments, and because of this, it is often easy to ignore the shortcomings of this view. However, we cannot fully understand the mind-body connection, consciousness or reality as long as all our thinking is based on 17th-century physics and philosophy, in which matter is treated as an unchanging, inert, "dead" body. Of course, there have been tremendous developments in physics during the 20th century, with modern physics, quantum physics, and relativity, but the materialistic worldview still relies on ancient physics, in part because there is no consistent, generally accepted view of how to explain it all.

Philosopher Thomas Nagel states in his book *Mind and Cosmos: Why the Materialist Neo-Darwinian Conception of Nature Is Almost Certainly False,* that reality is physical and spiritual, and the current materialistic worldview does not allow for such an approach. And how could it, for originally, at the birth of materialism, phenomena related to the mind and spirituality were decidedly excluded? It was known that the model is incomplete, but now, the same model seeks to explain phenomena that it was not originally intended to describe. It is time to abandon materialism, as it is incapable of explaining consciousness and related phenomena. Distinguished Australian neuroscientist and Nobel laureate Sir John Eccles states:

> ...the human mystery is incredibly demeaned by scientific reductionism, with its claim in promissory materialism to account eventually for all of the spiritual world in terms of patterns of neuronal activity. This claim must be classed as a superstition....

Naturally, ideas that present challenges to the prevailing perception of reality, such as in Nagel's, among others, have received much criticism. Many materialists have regarded Nagel's work as pseudo-scientific. However, Nagel is not alone in his thoughts, and the number of advocates of a different worldview has also increased among representatives of the natural sciences.

Materialism is able to explain our everyday phenomena well, in terms of physics and chemistry, for materialism and Newton's "classical" physics go hand in hand. However, when considering phenomena in which the mind and consciousness are involved, the situation changes. If we also perceive these phenomena through materialism, one should be able to explain them through matter.

From the point of view of physics, the subject is problematic, as it would require combining the level of reality we think of as spirit with that of matter. However, this is impossible according to many physicists, who argue that no particle has been found to show that the interaction of matter and spirit is possible. It is impossible to solve the problem of matter and spirit or reduce spirit back to matter or to show it as dependent on matter, because material and spiritual reality are already defined as opposed to each other. However, it should be obvious that everything we perceive is formed in our consciousness – partly in unconscious, partly in conscious processes – but in science this subject is almost taboo, and is not talked about. There has been a shift in power from the church, in the 17th century, to a science that determines reality but which is a reality that does not include subjectivity. It is believed rather that as measuring devices evolve, we approach an objective reality independent of observations.

Bernardo Kastrup, in his book *Why Materialism Is Baloney*, argues that the current debate in society between materialism and religion suggests that materialism is the only sensible explanatory model in science for our worldview and that the brain creates the mind. The brain can also be seen as an embodiment of the mind, just as a whirlpool is a local embodiment of water. The brain does not create mind, nor does the whirlpool create water. The brain is in the mind, not the mind in the brain. The mind can't be localized like the brain with its physical characteristics and processes. The brain is connected to our experience and is our interface to the world.

The physicist and philosopher Thomas Kuhn argues in his book *The Structure of Scientific Revolutions* that science involves paradigm shifts. Just as the greatest scientific inventions have not come by following familiar lines, so science does not flow smoothly from one picture of reality to another. The history of science sometimes includes major upheavals. The previous paradigm shift, to a materialistic and dualistic conception of reality, led to a revolutionary development in human history, having influenced both the Reformation and the Industrial Revolution. Reason and science were placed before spirit, mysticism, and religion. All indications are that we are now in a phase of change again.

The answer to the title question, then, is that we are not machines, but something much more. But can we ever really understand what reality is?

CHAPTER 3
CAN WE UNDERSTAND THE ESSENCE OF REALITY?

Our material world of appearances is an imperfect copy of the transcendent realm of Ideas or "forms."

—Plato

I sit outside meditating. It is the end of March and the blowing wind is still quite cold. I have a blanket on my shoulders, even though I am barefoot. The sun is shining, the birds are singing and with closed eyes, I can see colors, which become like a vortex that deepens the longer I meditate. I can smell the scents of spring and sense it everywhere. A thought pops into my mind: What would I feel if all my senses were excluded from this experience? I would not see, hear, smell, feel, nor taste. Would the feeling be the same as if I were asleep? Sometimes I intentionally use eye masks and earplugs when meditating to facilitate the perception of inner feelings. If all the senses were excluded, would it be easier to turn inward, to listen to your inner voice, to experience oneness, perhaps? What is really real, that which I experience with the senses or that which exists without the senses? Is it ever even possible for us to know what reality really is?

Plato and what REALLY IS

For those of us living in the Western world, it is almost self-evident that what I see, experience, hear, and feel is primary. Matter is real because I know it IS. I can sense it and it won't go away. But what if there is something even more fundamental, and matter is just a manifestation of this? It's easy to understand that the image in the mirror isn't really me, but an image of me. What if this is also the case with material reality? Perhaps what we see and perceive is just an image in the mirror of what it really is.

The sentence above from Plato summarizes well the idealistic worldview, which is at the extreme other end of the spectrum from the materialistic worldview. According to idealism, the world is fundamentally made out of ideas of "forms," as Plato described. Plato pondered the question of whether we could ever catch up with what REALLY truly is? Is our information just an abstraction, a mirror image of something that is more real? And where does our knowledge come from – is it based on experience (induction), reason (deduction) or intuition (abduction)? Plato discussed his doctrine of ideas in his dialogues *Republic, Phaedo, Phaedrus, Meno,* and *Parmenides,* but it is also mentioned in many other of his dialogues. In *Timaeus,* one of Plato's last dialogues,. he discusses the universe and its birth. In Greek philosophy, when searching for an answer to the essence of reality, one also seeks an answer to what is the essence of the universe. One seeks for oneness, not the diversity that our senses reveal to us. One seeks for that which is fundamental.

As early as *c.* 400 BC in *Timaeus,* Plato posed what is the most fundamental question in the whole of Western culture: What really IS? Or at least this opening to understanding the essence of reality should be the most important question, but it has been overlain with scientific certainties and lost from time to time over the last few centuries. Plato's thoughts have been discussed in philosophy, but now again they are more topical than ever, due to the development of modern physics, the unanswered question of consciousness, and our desire to understand the mind. We are currently in a transition out of the materialistic view of the world. Plato's thoughts in *Timaeus* are relevant again, to focus our attention on that fundamental question of what really is.

In *Timaeus,* Plato describes a dinner organized in honor of Socrates where the guests engage in philosophical discussion. Timaeus, who is best acquainted with astronomy and knows the most about the universe, considers the creation of the world and the question of causality:

> Was the heaven then or the world, whether called by this or by any other more appropriate name – assuming the name, I am asking a question which has to be asked at the beginning of an enquiry about anything – was the world, I

> say, always in existence and without beginning or created, and had it a beginning? Created, I reply, being visible and tangible and having a body, and therefore sensible; and all sensible things are apprehended by opinion and sense and are in a process of creation and created.

What is, thus, the reason for creating the world, and is it possible to understand this?

> Now that which is created must, as we affirm, of necessity be created by a cause. But the father and maker of all this universe is past finding out; and even if we found him, to tell of him to all men would be impossible. And there is still a question to be asked about him: Which of the patterns had the artificer in view when he made the world – the pattern of the unchangeable, or of that which is created? If the world be indeed fair and the artificer good, it is manifest that he must have looked to that which is eternal; but if what cannot be said without blasphemy is true, then to the created pattern.

Plato describes in *Timaeus* how the world has been created based on an eternal, unchanging model. According to him, there are no changes occurring in "that which REALLY IS"; instead it is constant and One. Of its nature Plato writes:

> Every one will see that he must have looked to, the eternal; for the world is the fairest of creations and he is the best of causes. And having been created in this way, the world has been framed in the likeness of that which is apprehended by reason and mind and is

> unchangeable, and must therefore of necessity, if this is admitted, be a copy of something. Now it is all-important that the beginning of everything should be according to nature. And in speaking of the copy and the original we may assume that words are akin to the matter which they describe; when they relate to the lasting and permanent and intelligible, they ought to be lasting and unalterable, and, as far as their nature allows, irrefutable and immovable – nothing less. But when they express only the copy or likeness and not the eternal things themselves, they need only be likely and analogous to the real words. As being is to becoming, so is truth to belief.

In *Timaeus*, Plato argues that since our world has been created according to an unchanging model, the best we can do is to present probabilities about reality. To understand reality, Plato presents three levels of existence:

1. The universe that truly IS. It is unchanging, original, unreachable, first and the beginning of everything.
2. The world we perceive with our senses, which is in a constant state of change. This world is created as a copy based on the original model.
3. That which has received existence.

Plato compares these states to a father, mother and child. "That which truly is," is the world of ideas, thus, the father, and it has always been and is rationally understandable, that is, rational. The state in which the existence has been received, is eternal and without form, and cannot be described in terms of reason, thus, it is irrational. According to Plato this is the mother. To make a copy of a statue, for example, a mold is made that makes it possible to make a copy of the original, which is thus the child. Our world was born when a mold was made according to the original world and the mold was then used to create a shape for our world, thus the world of our forms.

According to Plato, the foundation of the world's existence consists of a rational state, an irrational state, and "a birth." The rational and the irrational are dualistically opposites, but they merge with the third being into unity. The same dualism, according to Plato, is also reflected in how body and soul are opposites. The body is mortal and changes, while the soul is from the world of ideas, immortal and changeless.

Reality, "that which really is," the father in the analogy, thus has two essential characteristics, according to Plato and many other Greek philosophers, which deserve special consideration. "That which truly is" is one and unchanging. Is this at all the same reality that we are trying to understand today? We experience changes as real and perceive the world, reality, through our own senses. Even the whole of natural science is based on observations and measurements. However, there is something essential in the idea of the unchanging nature of reality – the idea of invariance – presented by Greek philosophers: In nature, changes are driven by the laws of nature, which appear to us to be unchanging, invariant. Invariance, then, is an aid to us that allows us to distinguish real from delusion. Thus, that which is unchanging is real. There are examples of this in modern physics as well, such as the theory of relativity. Its central principle, relativity, includes the invariance of the laws of nature: physics applies the same way in all the coordinate systems under consideration. The theory of relativity thus leads to an unchanging worldview. However, even relativity is just an assumption.

Since antiquity and the time of Aristotelian philosophy, our thinking has changed along with the development of the natural sciences, and observations are now considered as part of reality. What is observed is not just a "delusion of the senses" but seen as a manifestation of reality. Already Plato's pupil Aristotle thought that permanence and change belonged to one and the same worldly reality. Our understanding of reality increases as we make measurements, observations. Plato was able to formulate the challenge of understanding reality. One of the developers of quantum physics, physicist Erwin Schrödinger, states:

> [Plato] was the first to envisage the idea of timeless existence and to emphasize it – against reason – as a reality, more [real] than our actual experience.

So, the reality we seek to understand today is not invariant, unchanging, but subject to change. Therefore, reality and changes can also be studied by empirical, experimental, research methods. However, with experimental methods, we do not get information about the object itself, but we get information about what is affected by our measurement methods. Especially when studying the particle-level phenomena, the effect of observation on the results is quite extraordinary. I return to this in Chapter 5 where I discuss the effect of the observer.

It may be said, still, that what we seek is the same as in ancient times: We are still searching for what is unchanging, for what is real.

Mind is more fundamental than matter?

In colloquial, everyday language when someone is said to have "idealistic" thoughts, it often means something negative compared to the usual, "realistic" way of thinking. It is thought that the idealist is delusionally dedicated to his idea. An idealist does not understand practical issues because he is not a realist. But could idealism encompass what we really should understand? Could idealism provide answers to understanding the essence of reality?

Idealism has a far-reaching history not only in Greek antiquity but also in Eastern thought, especially in India. Indeed, several schools of Hindu and Buddhist philosophy can be characterized as idealistic. Perhaps the oldest reference to idealism is found in the Vedic text, Rig Veda, which mentions Purusha, the cosmic existence that is the basis of everything and that fills the entire universe.

Nowadays, idealism is most commonly referred to as subjective idealism, which is a metaphysical view claiming that only the mind and the mental really exist. Subjectivity here means that reality is completely dependent on the mind with which it is perceived. In the 18th century, especially thanks to the writings of the Irish philosopher and Bishop George Berkeley, subjective idealism gained support. Berkeley's view was that the world is made up of the minds of God and man, and existence means being perceived: "*Esse est percipi*" (to be is to be perceived), he stated.

The view of idealism is that reality is fundamentally spiritual, that is, of mind or produced by the mind. The mind is not the creation of the brain, as is thought in materialism, but on the contrary, the brain is of the mind. However, the mind in this context is different from our personal mind, it is something collective – our collective mind, or collective consciousness.

Idealism is different from solipsism, in which one thinks that only one's own conscious experiences exist, nothing else. In fact, according to solipsism, there are no conscious beings other than oneself. All others are only creations of their own mind, devoid of consciousness and existing only in their own consciousness. It is easy to think that dreams and characters in them could be creations of your own mind; could everyday reality also similarly be a big play of ideas?

Idealism also differs from panpsychism, which I mentioned earlier in the chapter about materialism. In panpsychism, it is thought that everything has consciousness, which is different from saying that all reality is in consciousness.

In our experience, we have our own minds. What we experience happens in our minds. Others have no connection to my mind. Although we experience our own experiences in our minds, Plato did not, however, claim reality was linked to mind, such as I have described above. Plato is often said to have represented objective idealism. The German philosopher Friedrich Hegel (1770–1831), among others, was also an objective idealist, although his ideas do not coincide with Plato's.

According to Hegel, all phenomena from consciousness to material bodies, and even states, are manifestations of the same universal spirit. Hegel combined all phenomena with history and described how we humans are also part of the historical process: We are born at a certain moment and inherit from our predecessors and contemporaries thought patterns, language, culture and often also the worldview, and as we live and learn, we develop them. According to Hegel, over time, all of these are seen as manifestations of spirit and are connected as part of the universal spirit through the process of feedback: the whole of reality, in his view, is in fact a historical process. Hegel saw the state as the culmination of everything, an absolute value, as opposed to, among other things, the ideas of another philosopher, Immanuel Kant (1724–1804), in which man is an absolute value and is served by the state. In many modern states, the state is thought to be for the people, but the practice is increasingly converging with Hegelian ideas.

From its many different branches, idealism could be summarized as follows:

- The perceived world has been created. Its model is a world that cannot be reached by any means. Nor can it be observed. We can only see the world that was created based on the model, for we are part of this world.
- Consciousness is more fundamental than matter. It follows that as consciousness changes, so does the physical world. The reasons for the changes in the physical world must therefore be sought at the level of the mind and consciousness.

The confrontation of materialism and idealism

Sir Arthur Eddington (1882–1944), an astrophysicist who became known for popularizing the theory of relativity, describes the difference between the materialist and idealist worldviews with the following example: When you touch a table near you, you feel its surface as hard and perhaps smooth. The material of the table forms the hardness and smoothness and the experience of the table is just a hallucination created by your mind, your brain. This is how the materialist thinks. If we look at the surface with an electron microscope, we can endlessly detect empty space and particles at distances from each other: protons, neutrons and electrons. So are there actually two different tables? The idealist thinks that the sensory experience of hardness arises in the human mind and the experience is thus fundamentally spiritual. So does the material substance exist at all?

What has begun to disrupt the supremacy of materialism, especially recently, is precisely the problems of the human mind and consciousness. According to materialism, we should also be able to explain spirituality based on the material world and using the concepts of materialism, but this has not been successful so far.

Dualism is one attempt to solve this problem. According to this school of thought, reality consists of both spiritual and material substances, one example of which is Descartes' notion that the human body belongs to the material world and follows the deterministic laws of nature, while the mind is part of the spiritual world and free of determinism. However, as we have seen, dualism has not proven to be a solution to the problems of mind and consciousness.

From the table example above, one feature of reality is outlined: reality is not necessarily immediately visible, but thinking may be needed to understand it. Thus, observation, measurements, and experience seem to be our only connection to reality. Both a scientific approach and experiential observation are needed. Each of us forms our own perception of reality, more or less aware of what our perception is based on. Ultimately, we are alone, each based in our own thinking. We each choose the vision of reality, the doctrine we trust, independently.

Are we not supposed to understand the essence of reality?

Although we want to understand things more, maybe we are not meant to see reality as it is. This is a point made by cognitive psychologist Donald Hoffman, in his book *The Case against Reality: Why Evolution Hid the Truth from Our Eyes*. Evolution has, in fact, favored perception that guides us to activities that keep us alive, such as reproduction, and hides the truth when necessary.

Hoffman cites the example of the Australian Jewel Beetle (Latin *Julodimorpha bakewelli*), which is dim, shiny and brown. The female is flightless, so the male must fly to it. The species almost became extinct, for the reason that the males became so interested in the beer bottles thrown into the wild, which were also dim, shiny, and brown, that they were trying to mate with the bottles. For thousands, even millions of years, males had found females based on their eyesight, looking for a female that is dim, shiny and brown, and the bigger the better. Australia eventually had to change the color of bottles to save these beetles from extinction.

If I see a snake, I don't lift it in my hand, and I don't step in front of the car driving towards me. These observations are my subjective experience of reality, objective reality is something else.

Physical objects in our world can be thought of as folders on a computer screen. Folders contain a lot of material, files, text, but on the computer screen, on the desktop, only a rectangular icon appears labeled with the name of the folder. The icon on the screen represents the material inside the folder. That is what we see, we see nothing else. However, you should not drag the folder to the Trash, as this will destroy all the material. In the same way, it is not wise to walk in front of a car.

Hoffman and his group have conducted several computer simulations in an effort to determine whether seeing reality as it is would be the best option for evolution. It turns out that is not. In all simulations, it was the least profitable option. Indeed, using the computer analogy, perhaps it is most optimal not to see the structure and components of a computer or software with its codes, but rather what we can accomplish with them. Evolution does not favor seeing reality as it is.

In fact, there are many ways to shape reality in the desired direction, and the direction is not towards the more real. For example, in the social media world, the aim of editing images is to create pictures that are suitable for the current purpose, for example by using emotionally appealing colors or by editing bodies to suit the prevailing attitudes. Maybe we don't even want to see reality as it is?

We imagine that seeing is objective, that we perceive objective reality when we see it as if through a camera's lens. However, this is not the case. The eye may be thought of as acting like a camera, but when we see, billions of neurons and trillions of synapses are activated in the brain. In fact, a third of the cortex is related to vision. According to brain scientists, the neurons and synapses in the brain create the shapes, colors and objects we see, that is, what we perceive at that very moment.

The answer to the question in the title "Can we understand the essence of reality?" is thus, that I can at least understand what I am unable to understand. In order to understand the essence of reality, we need to understand observation and what consciousness is, that is, how we experience it. We should be able to combine this knowledge with the scientific approach.

CHAPTER 4
WHAT IS THE CONNECTION BETWEEN CONSCIOUSNESS AND REALITY?

Deep down the consciousness of mankind is one.

—David Bohm

Most scientists can't explain consciousness in the brain, so they can't say that consciousness out of the brain is impossible.

—Stuart Hameroff

What is it that we all have, that our existence depends on, but that poses one of the biggest unresolved questions in modern science? It is consciousness. The question of consciousness is even said to be the last unresolved problem of science. However, it is not a small problem, for it includes everything; without understanding consciousness, we can't really understand anything else, because everything depends on consciousness. Without consciousness, we have no experience. How we see reality, the world, and ourselves all depends on consciousness.

So far, there is no unambiguous answer to what consciousness is. Perhaps the main reason for this is that the answer has often been sought through a materialistic lens. In this chapter, I highlight some new ideas – as well as some very old ones – that may elucidate the question of consciousness.

What does consciousness mean?

Even the term "consciousness" is not unambiguous, so it is necessary to define how I am using it.

Consciousness can mean *awareness*, in other words, whether one is awake in a conscious state, asleep or in a coma. Consciousness in science usually means awareness, a feature of living beings that involves subjectivity, experience of inner and outer worlds, and in some cases, as in human beings, self-understanding. Intelligence is also seen as part of consciousness. Awareness can also mean understanding the current state of things, or "being aware of how things are," which includes thoughts, feelings, imagination, and sensations. We also know that the conscious state "feels" experientially of something, that consciousness is qualitative.

Awareness can also refer to one's level of spirituality. One can speak, for example, of the expansion of awareness experienced as spiritual awakening. This sense is often accompanied by the idea that one can develop awareness and that understanding of one's own self and place in the universe can open up through various practices such as meditation.

All of these explanations of consciousness are united by the fact that there is always an observer, a subject, an entity experiencing them.

As we saw in the previous chapters, there is also the notion of consciousness in idealism, where consciousness is seen as the basis of reality. Consciousness in this context is something common, collective and transcendent – beyond the borders of an individual. This consciousness cannot be developed, as it is fundamental and greater than what we experience or are. We have no chance of reaching that consciousness, we have only our own faith that it exists. This consciousness has been called "Creator," "Oneness," "Source," "God," or "Brahman" and so on.

Philosopher David Chalmers, one of the most well-known researchers into the question of consciousness, in his book *Conscious Minds,* divides the topics on consciousness into two categories: Easy questions are those related to brain functioning, such as observation, learning, attention, and memory. What he calls "the hard problem of consciousness" is summed up in the question: "What does it feel like to be 'me'?" How do subjective experiences like the taste of strawberries, the blueness of the sky, or the feel of wet beach sand under your feet fit into an objective view of the world? This question of why we have "experience" is called the Qualia problem. In recent years, Chalmers has raised alongside the hard problem a meta-problem of consciousness: Do we actually even have a hard problem of consciousness? With this he seeks to question the assumptions related to consciousness and the perspective we often automatically choose.

In the summer of 2015, I participated in the "Towards the Science of Consciousness" (TSC) conference held in Helsinki, which was attended by Chalmers and a wide range of consciousness researchers in various disciplines. Consciousness is such a special topic that it unites scholars from many fields, from physicists, chemists, philosophers and computer scientists all the way to biologists, physicians and neuroscientists. TSC conferences have been held for more than 20 years, and finally, at the Helsinki conference, the decision was made to remove the word "Towards" from the name of the TSC conference and start referring to the science of consciousness. This change suggests the presumed superiority of materialistic thinking: It was not until 2015 that there was a consensus that consciousness is worthy of its own *scientific* discipline.

The hard problem of consciousness is a point of disagreement among researchers. Deepak Chopra also attended the Helsinki conference. Like Chalmers, he has questioned the existence of a hard problem of consciousness. If we ask the question in the form, "How does our biological body create consciousness?", our perspective is totally different than when we ask it in the form, "How does consciousness form the material world we perceive?" Then, the hard problem of consciousness disappears completely. It is only a hard problem from a materialist-physicalist ontological perspective. From this viewpoint, experimental observation and measurement is an experience, and one tries to explain it with another experience, the experience of consciousness: Observation takes place in the consciousness of the observer, that is, experience in experience.

Roughly, there are three different views on what consciousness is and how it arises. These were discussed more thoroughly in mind-body dualism chapter:

1. Materialism, that is the prevailing view of science: Body is primary and consciousness is the property of the brain. There is no separate

soul. According to the prevailing scientific view consciousness arose during evolution. Views on when and how consciousness came about vary. For example, has consciousness emerged only recently, when humans appeared, or earlier, when primitive organisms developed? The scientific panpsychist view is that consciousness is a property of matter.

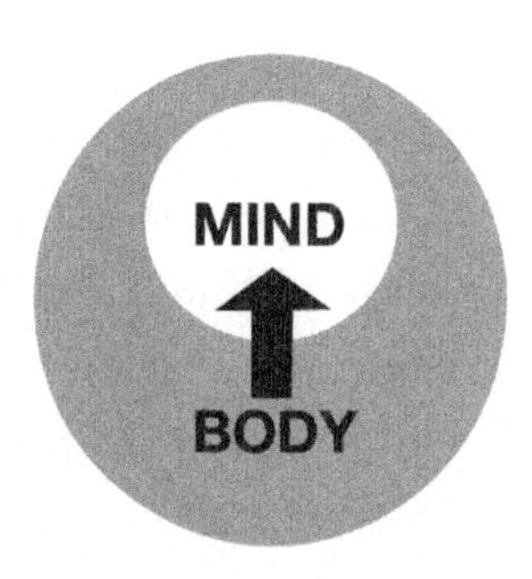

FIGURE 5. MATERIALISM.

2. Dualism: Body and mind (soul) are separate and interact with each other somehow. However, dualism is unable to explain how body and mind interact. Neither one is born from the other. The laws of physics that predominate in the material world do not influence mind (soul). Cartesian dualism, the views of religions and many spiritual ideologies think that consciousness has always been in the universe as the creator of everything.

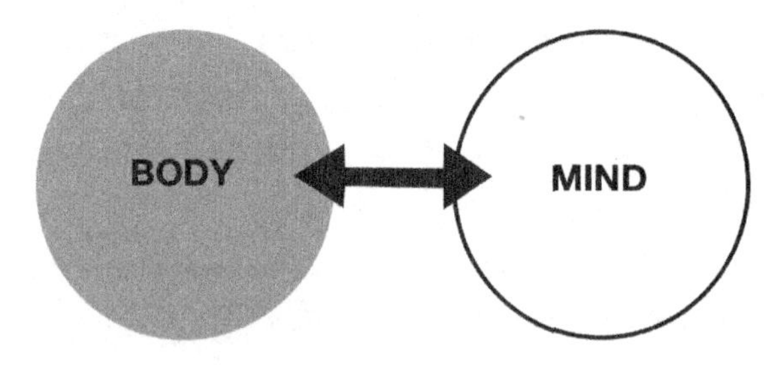

FIGURE 6. DUALISM.

3. Idealism: Consciousness is primary, matter secondary, as consciousness is the only thing that exists. Brains are only an interface, and consciousness is somewhere else.

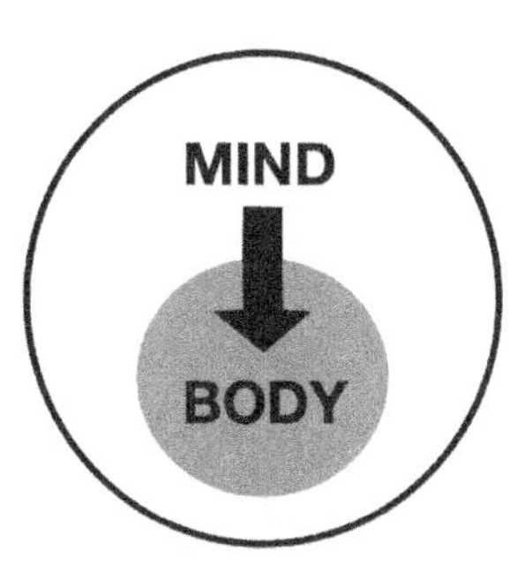

FIGURE 7. IDEALISM.

Is consciousness born in the brain?

At this point, the genome of many organisms is already known. The human genome was mapped in 2003. But even if the genome of an organism were known, at the system level it is unknown how an organism is formed and functions, even for the simplest organisms. The first multi-celled organism the whole genome of which was sequenced was a about a millimeter long, the transparent *C. Elegans* nematode. The worm has been living on Earth for millions of years. It has in total 959 cells, of which a third are neurons. Even the synapses, the structures permitting neurons to pass signals to other neurons, are known, but how the nematode forms and comes about as it does is unknown. There is a huge question mark between the structure and its consciousness – how it knows how to be a nematode – even though the genome of the worm was sequenced already in 1998.

Today, the best materialistic explanation for the birth of consciousness is considered to be the Integrated Information theory developed by neuroscientist and psychiatrist Giulio Tononi. In Tononi's theory, information is in fact the basis of everything, since the theory centers on the brain's capability to handle information in certain processes. Through fMRI, functional magnetic resonance imaging, it is possible to determine, for example, when the subject has an experience of a blue color and when not. Experiences can be seen differently in the brain. When a certain limit, which can be determined with experiments, is exceeded, the process can be considered conscious: There is an experience of the color blue. Consciousness is thought to be born as a result of connections between neurons. However, one cannot say what is the sufficient number of neurons to generate consciousness or why complexity would create consciousness. Tononi's theory doesn't in fact explain the birth of consciousness at all. It only describes in what kind of situations consciousness can be found. We don't know how a conscious experience, like the taste of chocolate in the mouth, is born in our brains.

PLANARIA

Planaria is a flatworm that can fully regenerate itself. If it is cut into, say, eight pieces, each one of the eight pieces has the ability to grow all the missing parts and thus eight fully formed individuals are born. When the individuals have reached their full size, the growth ends. Planaria worms are actually hundreds of millions of years old. Single cells can die, but the worm can renew them, thus keeping its form forever.

Planaria was studied in Michael Levin's laboratory at Tufts University. Planaria worms are clever and can be trained to learn a new habitat. What happens to learned knowledge when the worm's head is cut away? In a week Planaria grows a new head and is able to remember the original learned knowledge. The knowledge must therefore be stored somewhere else than in a brain.

A similar kind of regrowth happens in other animals, too, such as the tail of the viviparous lizard (Latin *Zootoca vivipara*) and the antlers of reindeer. Similar kinds of renewal happens in human beings, as well; for example, the liver can renew itself entirely, and a child's fingertip can regrow fully, if it is cut off before 7–11 years.

Where does the information for this kind of re-development exist? And where is the information that dictates when growth must stop? We are all first embryos, and gradually when cells divide, all the specialized organs are born. The information is not in the genome, as its function is to encode proteins, and not otherwise affect anatomy. The specialization of cells is not the answer either, since single-celled organisms also exist, which are specialized. The information needs to be elsewhere, but this is something we are currently unable to explain.

Besides Tononi, there are other researchers, such as psychologist and professor emeritus at London University Max Velmans, who find the brain's ability to process data to be an essential part of the explanation of birth of consciousness. It is easy to understand that the brain's ability to process data is exceptional and significant, but there is no proof that this would have anything to do with the emergence of consciousness. It also seems that regardless of what kind of lens scholars see through, or what kind of view on reality they bring to the object of study, they have the same problem we all do: an inability to step outside of one's own thinking, or break with one's own assumptions. It is easy to consider our own worldview as the only right one, because each one of us has experience only of the process that has led to our own worldview with its values and idea of reality.

There are of course other hypotheses and attempts to explain the world which are also compatible with materialistic thinking. For example, anesthesiologist Stuart Hameroff and quantum physicist Roger Penrose have developed a theory to explain the emergence of consciousness. Their hypothesis has not received wide acceptance so far, but it has generated a lot of discussion. (Hameroff is, by the way, one of the founders and organizers of the TSC conference I mentioned earlier, and every other year TSC is organized by the University of Arizona, where Hameroff is a professor.)

The theory of Penrose and Hameroff is called the Orchestrated Objective Reduction (Orch OR model) and it is based on microtubules found inside of neurons. Microtubules together with different kinds of filament form the cytoskeleton of neurons. Microtubules are known to participate in many functions in neurons, such as a cell's internal communication and cell division.

Penrose and Hameroff suggest that quantum phenomena are possible in microtubules and that consciousness is born as a quantum process orchestrated by microtubules, based on Penrose's interpretation of quantum physics, called objective reduction. The name of the model, "Orchestrated Objective Reduction," then, refers to this process. Each microtubule is like an independent quantum computer.

In quantum physics, the world is described by probabilities. All alternatives exist in quantum physics, and one of the various alternatives is selected as the reality we observe. According to some quantum physical interpretations, the consciousness of the observer is ultimately responsible for the selection. Penrose and Hameroff instead think that selecting means the same as consciousness; that is, the process of observing and selecting from all the possibilities is what we are calling consciousness. Their view is that consciousness follows from the physical world. Maybe it has always existed and been part of the physical laws in a way that is not known, even now. According to them, it is not necessary to encompass consciousness in current theories, but it should be possible.

Penrose's and Hameroff's model or some model like it could very well explain how consciousness is linked to the brain, as they definitely seem to have a connection. The model does not, however, verify materialism. It can explain how these are connected and the action mechanism of the user interface, but not the cause of it. So far, Penrose and Hameroff's model is not able to explain flawlessly the link between physics and biology.

Materialism is thus decidedly insufficient for understanding consciousness. It is unable to answer the question of how consciousness emerges, or many other questions related to the essence of consciousness. Materialism does not enable us to answer the question: At what stage do "I" become "You" if our cells are changed one by one? At what stage are there enough cell changes, so that the consciousness changes as well? Does it have to be 50% of cells changed? Or does consciousness change at all when cells are being changed?

We cannot explain how consciousness, something non-physical, is able to emerge from the physical, material world. The *philosophical zombie* thought experiment is often used in philosophy to demonstrate that a purely physical world (and the theory of physicalism) is impossible.

The idea of the philosophical zombie was deployed against physicalism in the 1970s by philosophers, the best known of whom more recently is David Chalmers. A philosophical zombie is a figure which is a copy of us but without consciousness, and thus, no experiences. It would be possible to build such a philosophical zombie, or even a whole world with nematodes, the genome of which is also already known. It is easy to imagine a world where each one of us has been replaced by a zombie. However, physicalism holds that in this kind of a world governed by physical laws, nothing can exist that arises from outside of the laws of physicalism. The emergence of consciousness would, thus, be impossible, and therefore also the existence of our own world.

We know, however, that our world exists, and based on this we can deduce that physicalism's model is untrue. Consciousness cannot be born in the brain.

Matter is consciousness

Philosopher Bernardo Kastrup offers an interesting theory about the essence of reality in his book *The Idea of the World* and in his doctoral dissertation *Analytic Idealism: A consciousness-only ontology*. Both books draw on scientific articles published in peer-reviewed scientific journals.

Kastrup's theory is based on idealism, that is, on the idea that consciousness is more fundamental than matter. His perspective is thus almost the opposite of Hameroff and Penrose's model that I described in the previous section.

Kastrup presents where materialism goes wrong: Because matter can be thought to consist of smaller units, it is thought that consciousness is likewise formed of smaller units. This is not the case, because in idealism, it is thought that there is only one consciousness; we don't speak of consciousness in the plural. Kastrup describes this oneness of consciousness and the conflict of separate human minds we experience through the metaphor of dissociative identity disorder. We humans, like any other living organisms, are dissociated, separated, from the universal consciousness in the same way an individual self is in dissociative identity disorder.

A person experiencing *dissociative identity disorder* (DID), or "multiple personality disorder" or "split personality disorder," experiences several side personality states, which can even be fully unaware of each other. Different personality states don't even necessarily have access to the same memories.

EVE WHITE, EVE BLACK AND JANE

Eve White was suffering of continuous severe headaches and blackouts, for which no physical reason was found. She had been in therapy with Dr. Thigpen already for several months in the hope of finding relief. Dr. Thigpen decided to use hypnosis to help Eve better remember the last blackout she had experienced. Eve had sent the doctor a letter, which was written in different handwriting. But Eve denied that she had sent any letter.

In the middle of the session Eve began holding her head, as if suffering severe pain, and then started to speak using a totally different voice, and presented herself as Eve Black: Eve White turned out to have DID. Eve Black was Eve White's other personality and Eve White's complete opposite: careless, feminine and childish. She was entirely her own personality with its own strengths and weaknesses: She for example got an allergic reaction from nylon pantyhose, while Eve White didn't react to at all.

Drs Thigpen and Cleckley studied the case for 14 months. Eve Black claimed that she had lived an entirely separate life since childhood with Eve White, and knew that Eve White didn't know of her. She also said that she is responsible for the headaches and blackouts. After eight months of therapy, a third person appeared: Jane, who seemed to be a compromise of the two personalities. Eve White's and Jane's EEG tests had similar alpha rhythm, while Eve Black's was considerably faster. Jane knew about the other two personalities. During the therapy sessions Jane started taking more space from Eve White, and Eve Black caused less trouble.

Different personalities can even be so different that they may speak different languages or have different physical problems. In one case, where a women had adulthood diabetes, depending on which personality was dominant, she needed a different dosage of insulin.

CASE OF A WOMEN WHO HAD LOST HER SIGHT

Strasburger and Waldvogel reported a peculiar case in 2015. A German woman had been in an accident when she was 20 years old. Due to this accident she slowly lost her sight entirely. When she came to therapy, she was 35 years old and completely blind. She even needed a guide dog to help her in her everyday life.

During therapy it was found out that the woman had DID and 10 subpersonalities, of which some were able to see normally and some were blind. Strasburger and Waldvogel used EEG to verify that the woman's brain functioned entirely normally when a seeing person was dominant. Brain areas that activate when a person sees functioned well. When a personality that wasn't able to see came through, there was a clear change in the brain. The change could happen very fast, and it was as if they were suddenly studying the brain of an entirely other person. When a seeing person again stepped in, those areas of the brain that are linked to seeing were activated. During the therapy sessions, the woman's ability to see was restored in the dominant personality.

It is also known that different personalities can be dominant in a person at the same time. They can, for example, see the same dream but from different perspectives, from different roles. As in the case of DID, according to Kastrup, we are all part of the universal consciousness and emerged as separate "*alters*" of the universal consciousness. We can infer that the mind we experience, our personal consciousness or mental functioning, doesn't have borders and speak of an expansive, universal mind, in the same way we know that the world exists outside of our house, even though we don't see it exactly at that moment. We don't visually observe the world outside our house constantly, but we can assume it exists, even when we are not looking. This is a natural assumption based on our experience. It is even self-evident, unlike the assumption of the prevalent materialistic thinking that everything in our world, even our consciousness and mind, is fundamentally formed of matter.

In fact, the world that is composed solely of matter is mindless (in both meanings of the word, without mind and unaware). Such a world, as in the previous example, is not a natural assumption based on experience of what is already known. Something completely different is assumed: a parallel universe, which is fundamentally independent of our own universe and different than ours. It is something we can't even think of, because mental images are products of mind and experiential, and thus they don't belong to the material world. This idea requires a much bigger change in thinking than to expect that our world exists outside of our house and that we can speak of expanded, collective, universal mind.

Why are we thus observing and experiencing one collective material world and not only movements of mind? Kastrup describes in his model how an *alter*'s mental state consists of our own mind, expanded mind – that is the universal mind – and an interface, where our own mind interfaces with the expanded mind. Kastrup describes this interface with Markov's "Blanket" model, and states that it equals the physical world experienced by each *alter*. Many phenomena in nature can be modelled using Markov's Blanket model, such as the functioning of a cell membrane or skin. Each *alter* at the interface of our own mind and expanded mind constructs their own physical world based on observations. However, we all experience only one reality. When an *alter* interacts with expanded mind, it indirectly receives information from other *alters*. The physical worlds we all construct are thus not separate from each other.

According to Kastrup's theory, consciousness thus explains our material world:

> The world we perceive is made of consciousness. What we call matter is consciousness itself. ... Consciousness is a fundamental building block of reality, like space-time and the properties of matter.

It is interesting that according to Kastrup we are all one, of one whole. Consciousness is one and it connects us all. In reality, there is no separateness, no competition or conflict, because we are all basically one and the same. Maybe now is simply a time for us to experience separateness and not the pure, unconditional connection to each other. At some other point, the situation may be different and we can return to experiencing that universal connection.

Consciousness is collective?

Markov's Blanket model could explain how minds may "unite." There clearly exist situations when the connection between us seems to be so strong that our minds seem as one. Markov's Blanket may be porous, permeable, permitting minds to unite, but according to the model, minds cannot be in connection all the time. The model could also explain how telepathy and many other phenomena categorized as belonging to parapsychology work: It is possible for minds to unite in certain circumstances momentarily.

Psychiatrist and psychoanalyst C.G. Jung was the originator of the concept of *collective unconscious,* which he defined as behavior and a substratum of ideas common to a certain social group. He was referring to how individuals of the same species share information as if from one common unconscious mind. According to Jung this was shown, for example, in dreams, fairy tales and myths that share features in common across different cultures, and also in certain archetypes he defined. Knowledge of the character of archetypes is transmitted to us unconsciously.

One of the first and the most important archetypes is that of the mother, which is associated with positive, maternal love and warmth. One example of collective unconscious is LoBue and DeLoache's study in 2006, where it was noted that one-third of British six-year-old children were afraid of snakes, even though they are rare in the British Isles. Children had never encountered snakes in traumatic situations, but were still distressed.

JACKDAWS, WHISTLE AND YELLOW UMBRELLA

Animal trainer Tuire Kaimio was training a jackdaw and its friends for a movie. The main character bird learned to link the sound of a whistle and a yellow umbrella to treats and that it needed to fly to a tree nearest the umbrella. All its friends did the same thing even though these individuals had not been trained.

Over five years later, the trainer was visiting the same shooting locations and heard familiar noises of jackdaws from one tree. She decided to see if the jackdaws still remembered the trick. She had a whistle and she decided to use a yellow plastic bag as a replacement for an umbrella. A huge number of jackdaws arrived right away at the location. They seemed to fly there from far away. They must have received the information somehow "wirelessly"; perhaps the information was transmitted in a common information field – through a collective unconscious. How did the birds that were hundreds of meters, even kilometers, away receive the information? How did they know to arrive instantly, when the trainer approached the tree? How did they know that there were treats on offer?

Collective consciousness can also be seen as a behavior which is common to a particular social group. One example of collective consciousness or group consciousness is flocks of birds, schools of fish or hives moving in a group seamlessly like one entity. Flocks have been studied and modeled, and it is impossible to explain based on ordinary senses, how information flows between individuals in a group. Birds fly as a group as if they know where each one's place is, but at the same time, they are moving as a whole, as one entity. The exchange of information has to be so fast that it cannot be through sound. Lately, scholars have been more inclined to think that in addition to the birds directing their flight through the movements of several of their fellow companions, their movement is one indication of group consciousness.

One scholar who is open to thinking like this is biologist Rupert Sheldrake, professor at the University of Cambridge. According to Sheldrake, it seems that animals are capable of forming a very tight bond in a group, as if telepathically transmitting information to each other. Sheldrake explains this phenomenon with a model very similar to Jung's collective unconscious, called morphic fields. Sheldrake has studied the relationship between humans and their pets, and the so called paranormal abilities observed in animals. A large proportion of pets, for example, sense when their owners are coming home. Dogs seemed to sense it more often than cats, although Sheldrake suspects that cats are just not that willing to show what they are sensing. All the factors that earlier were thought to explain this phenomena were excluded in the study. The owners came home using different cars, taxis and other vehicles and at different times, so that animals could not hear their owner's familiar car or learn their homecoming time based on daily rhythm.

According to Sheldrake's theory a pet is able to form together with its owner a common information field, which he calls a morphic field. The pet is able to receive information telepathically through this field. Sheldrake's hypothesis is that there are ensembles in nature that share the same system field characteristic for that set. Each self-organizing system is also a whole formed from parts and these parts are also entities of a lower level.

At each level the morphic field forms the properties of each self-organizing whole, making it more than the sum of its parts. Such a field is responsible for the physical structure of an individual, for example. According to Sheldrake, fields of perception, behavior and mental activity are responsible for perception, behavior and mental functions. There are fields of crystals and molecules responsible for them, fields for organization of communities and cultures, and so on.

Sheldrake's hypothesis has inspired much discussion, but it hasn't received wider acceptance yet. Sheldrake's morphic fields hypothesis greatly resembles Kastrup's Markov model, in that both are based on the idea of information transfer in certain situations. How, for example, does the hair of a striped or patterned animal, like a cat, dog or zebra, know when to switch colors? Colored areas have clear lines, and a separate hair can change color even when growing. According to science, hair is dead material, and doesn't include molecules that could transfer information. All this must indicate that the information is somewhere else, not in the genes. The information needs to be in some kind of a field or energy body. It could very well be that there is a field behind everything that transfers information.

The hypothesis that information is transferred through a field has been suggested by many other scholars, too. In her book, *The Field,* Lynne McTaggart presents the views of several scholars on the field hypothesis. McTaggart has also written a book, *The Power of Eight,* on our group effect: It seems that when a group of people shares the same intention, the effect multiplies. We seem unconsciously to strengthen each other's intention and support each other. I will return to this topic later in this book.

Could it be that in certain situations, in certain circumstances, the connection between us becomes stronger and we are able to receive information from our common, unified field – from our collective consciousness? Many of us have experienced something like having a person suddenly come to our mind and finding out later that they were in trouble. Is it possible that many phenomena categorized as parapsychological, when they cannot be explained based on the prevailing paradigm, are an indication of collective consciousness and the connection between us?

Consciousness = Qi

Consciousness is considered to be something all-encompassing, all-pervading and ubiquitous. There have been other concepts throughout history that have been described with similar terms.

Aether's properties were described with these adjectives in the 18th and 19th centuries. Aether had been talked about since ancient times, and science tried to explain the behavior of electric bodies with the concepts of field and aether. A medium was needed to explain the behavior of light, and aether was also used to explain what we now know as gravity. Aether was invisible and massless, and it permeated the entire universe. Sometimes aether was understood as matter, sometimes as immaterial field which suffused everything. Later, our understanding of the behavior of light and its dual wave-particle character, and the theory of relativity, removed the need for aether. However, aether didn't disappear entirely, and different kinds of aether theories have popped up from time to time. Many of my fellow students from the Physics department of the University of Helsinki in the 1990s probably remember a man named Kauko Nieminen, who had his own aether flux theory. Nieminen actively promoted his theory in different departments of the university and at university events. More recently, Physics Nobel Prize laureate Frank Wilczek has brought up the concept of aether. He points out that space is not an empty, passive container of everything, but a dynamic network, a modern aether. Actually, Einstein admitted in 1920, that the theory of relativity isn't in contradiction with the idea of aether. Space-time as a concept is a modern version of aether.

Swedenborg and a force arising from infinity. Swedish philosopher, theologist, mystic and scholar Emanuel Swedenborg's (1688–1772) influence on many other philosophers' work can be seen even today. Swedenborg contributed plenty of inventions in different disciplines; for example he invented a "flying machine" and submarine and described how blood, the brain and nervous system worked and how the soul is linked to the body. Many of his hypotheses have been proven correct. As was typical for that era, scholars approached any topic openly, and Swedenborg wrote, in one instance, a study on the melting and mining of iron, copper and brass, and next, a theory of the cosmos seeking to understand how God created a man and how the soul and body are linked to each other. Swedenborg's visions and dreams were exceptional, and his gifts as a visionary were known all over Europe. When Swedenborg visited the court of Sweden, Queen Louisa Ulrika presented Swedenborg with a question she wanted him to ask of her departed brother. Swedenborg returned to the court three weeks later and told the answer to the Queen. According to the Queen, Swedenborg reported things that only her brother knew. Swedenborg's view was that our existence, purpose and development are dictated by the soul, which is a force that flows from infinity to us. Swedenborg suggested that the soul is connected to the body in the cortex, which is thus, the unifier of the world of spirit and matter.

Animal magnetism, i.e. mesmerism. Named for German doctor Franz Anton Mesmer, this view held that all life is directed by an invisible natural force, which also has an effect on the physical world, as in healing. Mesmer's theory was accepted in 1766 in Vienna as a doctoral dissertation, which shows his ideas were not abnormal for that era. The theory was based on the general notion of the influence of the moon and planets on humans. The effect had certain cycles, such as the phases of the moon, positions of planets and stars and a link to gravity. Animal magnetism was something that suffused the entire universe. Mesmer thought these changes could also have an effect, an interference, on humans. He first captured these interferences using magnets, until he noticed that healers themselves had a healing effect on their healees.

Odic force. In 1840, Baron Carl von Reichenbach studied the nervous system of humans and discovered a new force that seemed to have a connection to electricity, magnetism and heat. He named this the Odic force, after the ancient Scandinavian god Odin. Many seemed to be sensitive to this vital force, and it was thought to be part of plants, animals and humans. It was possible to see the Odic force in the dark as colorful auras, but only very sensitive and experienced observers were able to do that. Odic force didn't seem to have a connection to breathing, but instead affected electromagnetic fields. Reichenbach stated it was possible to channel Odic force to others especially through the palms, mouth and forehead, and the force seemed to have attracting and deflecting sides. Reichenbach published his studies in an article in the scientific magazine *Annalen der Chemie und Physik*. Odic force was studied later, in the 19th century, at the University of Edinburgh in the context of hypnosis, with an intention to prove that Odic force and phenomena described by Mesmer and Swedenborg were all of the same origin.

Élan vital. French philosopher Henri Bergson describes in his early 20th-century book *Creative Evolution, élan vital,* or *life force* (or *vital impetus* or *vital force*), which he connected closely to consciousness, saying it is the "*intuitive perception of experience and of internal passage of time.*" Many cultures through history have held an idea of a *universal life force,* which is also called *Chi, Qi, Prana, Mana, Pneuma, Archeus* and so on. These often have a connection to breathing.

Purusha. An idea from Eastern philosophies, including the trinity found in Hinduism, which is said to be the source of all consciousness: *sat* (truth), *chit* (awareness), *ananda* (bliss), this concept describes unity and perfection, and the meaning of everything. Some honor this idea as Brahman, the ultimate reality behind the universe and the gods. According to the Upanishads, the fourth part of the Vedic Sanskrit texts: "*The highest truth is that behind everything is a divine omnipresent consciousness.*" Eastern philosophies also mention Purusha and Prakriti. Purusha means pure consciousness, the unformed side of reality. Purusha also refers to that awareness in which reality is being observed. Prakriti and Purusha are complementary terms. Prakriti means nature and the manifested reality, everything that exists. Together they form the experience of reality, oneness, perfection and the meaning of everything.

The elementary particle field of current modern science. Elementary particles are particles that don't consist of other particles and don't have their own structure. Atoms are made up of electrons, protons and neutrons. An electron is an elementary particle, but protons and neutrons consists of even smaller particles, called quarks. It is thought that there are elementary particles everywhere in the universe, and they are often observed only when they interact with other particles. According to the current prevailing model, elementary particles also act as intermediate particles, or force carriers, of basic interactions; a photon is an intermediate particle of electromagnetic radiation. String theory is a model in which elementary particles are considered as vibrating strings and the whole universe is thought of as consisting of these strings. The field of elementary particles is thus thought of as all encompassing, all pervading and ubiquitous, as consciousness is also thought to be. However, there are no attempts currently in science to connect the field of elementary particles to consciousness, as the current worldview of materialism cannot accommodate such a connection. It is still widely thought that matter is the basis of everything. Physicist John Hagelin, at Harvard University, has suggested, however, that the unified field suggested by string theory means the same as the unified field of consciousness, which is also proposed by Indian guru and developer of the Transcendental Meditation technique, Maharishi Mahesh Yogi.

Each era shapes things into that mold and concepts it finds to be appropriate for that time. Maybe we've been talking about the same thing, but with different concepts and from slightly different perspectives? We have a need to describe and manage the world using concepts. But maybe concepts restrict our thinking, and we should let go of them. We often think that the way we see the world currently is the whole truth and that there is nothing better coming in the future.

Consciousness and experimentalism

According to Deepak Chopra, besides matter, we have to learn to understand experience as well, to understand reality. In his view, matter and experience are both different forms of consciousness underlying our world.

Everything that exists, exists only through our conscious experiences. We experience reality in our awareness, and consciousness is always experienced from inside it, by an observer, or subject, that is continuous with it. We cannot create an objective view of it.

Galileo Galilei wrote:

> I think that tastes, odors, colors, and so on are no more than mere names so far as the object in which we locate them are concerned, and that they reside in consciousness. Hence if the living creature were removed, all these qualities would be wiped away and annihilated.

It is possible using neuroimaging to study what kind of effect the experience of sensing has in our brains. However, these measurements cannot fully determine the location of a particular mental activity in the brain. Brain activity in a particular area may also be related to the performance of another function, or that function may have other neural conditions that are not measured by imaging. However, neuroscience has undeniably shown a link between conscious functions in the brain and the central nervous system.

Neuroimaging provides information about another person's experience so it can be considered as "third-person" data. It is even more challenging to receive objective information on how we ourselves are experiencing, which is so-called "first-person" data. The conscious state is experienced personally as sensation.

While writing this book, I have come across the term phenomenology on many occasions, especially in the context of experiences and the question of being. Phenomenology is the study of consciousness from the perspective of a person's own world of experiences. It seeks an understanding of consciousness and human experience, and through this also the meaning of experience. In Western philosophy, phenomenology begins with Hegel (1807), who considered the goal of studying different phenomena to reach the absolute and metaphysical all-encompassing Spirit. It was Edmund Husserl, in the 20th century, who advanced phenomenology, the basis of which is intuition as a way to understand experience. He called this 'phenomenological reflection' and tried to find the essence or invariant qualities of phenomena and experiences through the phenomenological method in which one's consciousness of something partially constitutes it.

Generally speaking, there is no consensus among phenomenologists on how the method should be used and what it all means. The development of science in the 20th century may be seen to have a similar approach to understanding reality as that of phenomenology: For example, Martin Heidegger, one of the predominant developers of phenomenology in 20th century, thought of it only as a way to receive information about the world, but not a way to access *"understanding of Being"* or "existence." Heidegger's German term *Dasein* or Being is a fundamental concept in his existential philosophy. Phenomenology has been criticized a lot for its "non-scientific" approach. For example, many scientists think that the "first-person" subjective approach of phenomenology is not compatible with the scientific "third-person" objective approach. Maybe now, in the 2020s, the world is ready for phenomenology's first-person approach. Through it, the possibilities for understanding and finding meaning through experimentalism could open up to an even larger group of people.

Many spiritual seekers or persons that have experienced so-called spiritual awakening are also unknowingly practicing phenomenology, as phenomenology holds the possibility that consciousness can be trained and developed. Phenomenology has a lot in common with Buddhist philosophy, such as a similar respectful attitude towards life. As a first-person study of experience, it also plays a part in other wisdom traditions of Eastern origin that theorize about consciousness.

According to the Indian tradition of Vedanta, it is thought that we are *Atman*, the Sanskrit term for "inner self or soul," which is close conceptually to consciousness, not mind and body. We have to practice *atma vichara*, self-searching, or self-inquiry, to discover what we truly are. *Atma vichara* leads further to self-realization.

Paramahansa Yogananda describes in his book *Autobiography of a Yogi* those goals that he sees as the most important ones in life. One of these is to share information of those precise techniques that may lead to achieving a personal experience of God. The meaning of life is to expand the limited mortal human consciousness to God-awareness or universal consciousness, which he sees as the origin of everything, unchanging and all-pervading. According to Yogananda, through our own spiritual practices, we can gain understanding of reality, of what truly IS.

When I visited the Modern Contemporary (Moco) Museum of Amsterdam, I became familiar with the work of artist Daniel Arsham. He has been color blind from birth. In 2015, he received glasses, through which he was for the first time able to see all colors. Until then, his art had consisted solely of gray shades, lines, materials and textures. Colors now filled his works. After a while, he decided to leave the glasses off, since he felt that his new reality was like a virtual world and that it was leading in a wrong, and even disturbing, direction.

Are we all just viewing reality through different kinds of glasses? Maybe we don't need to search for a diversity of views but instead try to simplify as Arsham did? How can we ever be sure that experiential knowledge is true?

One morning when I woke up I kept wondering about the dream I had just had. The dream was an amazing adventure, where I was running through the narrow streets of an old town, occasionally knocking on wooden doors, behind each of which opened more and more imaginary scenes, stairs, palaces, halls, and so on. Sadly, I almost immediately forgot the plot. I simply remembered that I was looking for a place to hide the treasure chest I was carrying. It was so heavy that I remembered it well. I was wondering: If we are able to create in our minds a dream reality such as the one I had just experienced, which seemed to be so true, wouldn't it be perfectly plausible that a more comprehensive and fundamental consciousness could create a reality such as that we are experiencing right now? I kept wondering, too, how we are able to create in a dream such perfect stories, ensembles that are almost logical, causal, in the same way we experience when we are awake. At least by the dream's logic, it all makes sense, or has the feeling of making sense. We don't have a clue about the plot in advance, although we apparently create it by ourselves. Doesn't it make you think that we are also creating our everyday reality?

In the context of everything I have written here in this book, the best possible explanation of our reality seems to derive from the supposition that consciousness is fundamental. This can be supported using the principle of Occam's razor, or the "law of parsimony," which says the simplest explanations of unknown phenomena are to be preferred to complex explanations. The term Occam's razor, associated with the thinking of English Franciscan friar and philosopher William of Occam, refers to his preference for theoretical simplicity and trimming away extraneous assumptions. There is no need to assume anything more than necessary. The simplest theory is probably the best one.

The assumption that consciousness is fundamental seems a perfect basis on which to establish reality. One must only understand the subjective experience that is observing.

CHAPTER 5
OBSERVATION AFFECTS REALITY?

What you think matters, in fact it forms matter.

—Vajra Ghanta Gadan

Reality is a challenging subject to study. The conventional methods of science won't work, because we cannot distinguish the object of study from its observer.

As a matter of fact, is objective observation ever truly possible, whatever the object to be observed is? We as observers are always part of the same reality as that which we are observing. In fact, the situation is the same as when we are measuring the temperature of the water in a bowl using a thermometer: When the thermometer is added for measuring, you are no longer measuring the temperature of the original water+bowl system, but instead the water+bowl+thermometer system. The situation is changed from the original set-up. We cannot receive information about the temperature of the water+bowl system using a thermometer. Maybe we always also need to take into account our own effect on the reality that we are observing?

Consciousness collapses the wave of possibilities?

The observer's effect is also one of the most fundamental questions of quantum physics. Observing in physics means measuring, or reading the result of what is being observed.

Quantum physics changed our view of reality, and we still don't fully understand all of its implications. At the end of 19th century, there was a growing number of phenomena in physics that could not be explained using the "old" Newtonian classical physics. The model of classical physics is a set of laws, which describe the movement of objects when they are affected by forces. One such phenomenon that was challenging to describe was black-body radiation. A black-body is a theoretical object that absorbs all incoming electromagnetic radiation, such as light, without reflecting anything back from its surface or letting anything through. In physics it is an important phenomenon, because it describes the simplest interaction between matter and radiation, that is thermal radiation.

In classical physics, electromagnetic radiation is thought of as a continuous phenomenon, as wave motion. Until then, radiation was assumed to be continuous, as it usually is in nature. If we attempt to explain black-body radiation using classical physics, the power of the radiation that the body emits should be greater the shorter the wavelength of the radiation. The power of the radiation should, thus, approach infinity as the wavelength approaches zero. If this were the case, all objects around us would emit life-threatening amounts of X-rays and gamma radiation into their surroundings. So our experience shows that this cannot be the case. The model of classical physics doesn't fit the experimental results. The behavior of the hot radiating material cannot be explained unless we assume light propagates by leaps and bounds, as physicist Max Planck did.

To explain this phenomenon, Planck proposed a hypothesis in 1900: electromagnetic radiation, such as light, is emitted as *energy packets*, which he called *quanta*.

If we assume that electromagnetic radiation exists only as quanta with a certain size, which is proportional to the frequency of the radiation, the phenomenon can be explained. The black-body is assumed to consist of particles that vibrate more strongly the higher their temperature and energy. Planck made the assumption that, contrary to the rules of classical physics, in which all energy states were possible, only certain energy states are allowed. In this way he was able to derive a law of radiation corresponding to reality, that is, experimental results. The solution to the problem proposed by Planck in 1900 was anomalous, but proved to be correct. Using the same hypothesis, it was also possible to explain, among other things, the photoelectric phenomenon for which Einstein received the Nobel Prize in Physics in 1921.

Planck's assumption of quanta, i.e., energy packets that can only exist in certain energy states, initiated the development of quantum mechanics. Sometimes light behaves like particles and sometimes like waves. And what

is even more strange, in quantum physics, the observer seems to have a completely revolutionary effect on the results: The observer of the experimental result – the measurer – influences what is observed, as in the case of light and whether particles or waves are seen. Light behaves like a particle if the flow of light is monitored, and like a wave if not.

ZENO AND THE INFINITE JOURNEY

The observer has an effect on that which is being observed. It is not only recent physicists, but also Ancient Greek philosopher Zeno who contemplated this possibility. Zeno reasoned that for an arrow to get to its destination, it has to first travel half of its journey. To be able to travel half of the journey, the arrow has to first travel half of that journey, and half of that journey and so on. The arrow must be able to travel an infinite amount of half-journeys to be able to get to even half of the way, and thus it is impossible for it to reach its destination!

In a 1977 article, physicists Misra and Sudarshan proposed the Zeno effect adapted to the quantum world: According to quantum theory, when a radioactive particle decays after a certain time, the end result is a different state than the initial state. However, observation affects the particle, as described earlier, and the particle doesn't change its state when it is being observed. Misra and Sudarshan propose it is possible that if the particle is being observed continuously, it never decays or changes its state! The phenomenon, called the quantum Zeno effect, has also been found experimentally, and it really happens in nature.

An analogous phenomenon is referred to in quantum physics as tunneling. This is a phenomenon where a particle can change its state from one to another, even though according to classical physics it shouldn't have enough energy for this change. It is thus said that the particle "tunnels" through the potential energy barrier that separates the two states. If the tunneling happened in the real world, to be able to get to the other side of the wall in front of you, you wouldn't search for the gate, but instead would go directly through the wall and simply appear on the other side. Even though the phenomenon is impossible according to classical physics, the particle tunnels anyway. If you follow the particle, it doesn't happen, but if you don't, then it happens.

The whole mystery of quantum physics is crystallized in these experiments: How is it possible that simply following the experiment, that measuring or observing, can affect the result?

How, then, does measurement, or observation, change the situation? In quantum physics the world is described with probabilities. All the probable alternatives exist, and for each one of them a probability of being realized can be expressed (Figure 8).

The probability is described by a wave function or a probability distribution. When measurement is performed, the observation selects one of the options to occur. It is said that the observation collapses the wave function to a certain state, and the rest of the options disappear and are no longer possible. The wave function disappears at exactly the same moment when the observation is done. The behavior of the wave function can be described using the motion equation of quantum physics – the Schrödinger equation – and the materialized particle using classical physics. None of the theories in physics, however, describes the moment when the observation is done and the reality emerges from the possibilities.

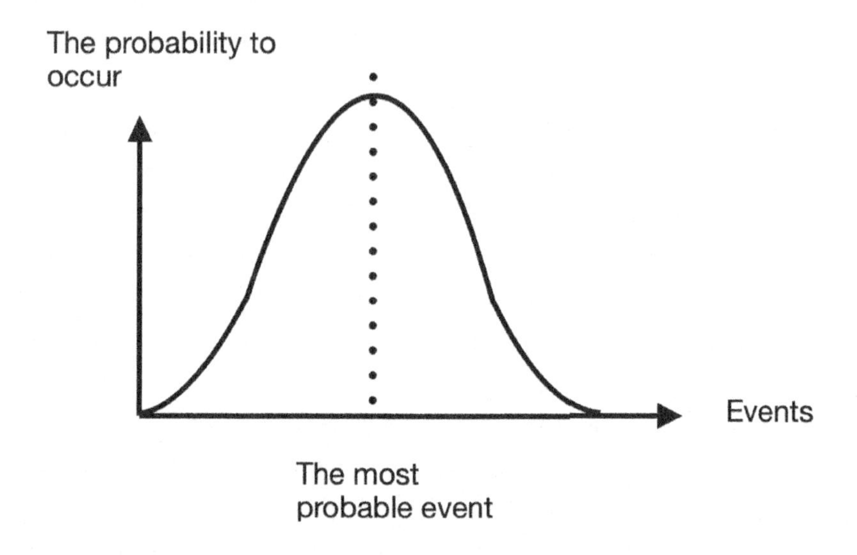

FIGURE 8. THE PROBABILITY DISTRIBUTION OF AN EVENT. THE MOST PROBABLE EVENT HAS BEEN MARKED WITH A DOTTED LINE.

One famous example to illustrate this is the thought experiment called Schrödinger's cat. In the experiment, a cat is inside a closed box with a closed flask of poison, and a small amount of radioactive substance. The radioactive substance can decay within an hour, but there is an equal probability that it won't. If it decays, it emits a particle that opens the flask of poison and the cat dies. As long as we don't open the box, all the probable possibilities exist and the cat is both alive and dead, thus the state is a combination of these two states, that is a superposition or mixture. Both states are equally probable. When the box is opened and the observation is made, either one of the realities is being realized and the other alternative disappears.

When the observer observes, a choice is made. All other possibilities disappear and only one reality remains. One can even say that the observation, thus, forces the reality to emerge and the observer "creates" the reality they observe. Things are "real" only when someone observes them. This is known to occur at least at the particle level. Thus, unlike in classical physics, which seeks objective truth by eliminating all perturbations, among other things the influence of the measurer, in quantum physics it is known that this is not even possible.

All physicists generally agree on the above: The act of measurement, thus, the observation, collapses the wave function and a certain reality is observed.

But what causes the wave function to collapse to a certain reality and to an actual body, i.e. to a particle? This question is the so-called measurement problem, which many interpretations of quantum physics try to answer. Physicists and philosophers haven't been able to agree on which of the interpretations best describes reality.

The interpretational problems started at the very beginning, when the founders of quantum physics tried to find consensus on what kind of theory it should be. Some sought a clear mathematical theory. Attempts were made to avoid over-interpretation. Niels Bohr and Werner Heisenberg, to whom the development of quantum physics is often attributed, eventually refused to take a position at all on the question of reality and on what quantum theory truly means. They relied on their own concepts of complementarity and inaccuracy. I will return to these concepts later in this book. There weren't, however, any real differences in the views of reality among the developers of quantum physics, as the following sentences well describe:

- Werner Heisenberg and Eugene Wigner: "*The wave function describes our knowledge and its reduction, or collapse, occurs when we 'become aware' of a particular outcome.*" Wigner had even more idealistic ideas than Heisenberg, as he considered the mental side of reality as primary over the material side.
- Niels Bohr: "*When it comes to atoms, language can be used only as in poetry. The poet, too, is not nearly so concerned with describing facts as with creating images and establishing mental connections.*"
- Bohr also stated: "*There is no quantum world, there is only an abstract quantum mechanical description. When we measure something we are forcing an undetermined, undefined world to assume an experimental value. We are not measuring the world, we are creating it.*"
- Max Planck: "*I regard consciousness as fundamental. I regard matter as derivative from consciousness. We cannot get behind consciousness.*

Everything that we talk about, everything that we regard as existing, postulates consciousness."

I have to mention the most familiar interpretation of quantum physics, the Copenhagen interpretation, which was proposed by many of the developers of quantum physics, especially Heisenberg and Bohr. Oskar Klein and Wolfgang Pauli had an especially important role in reconciling the differences of opinion between Bohr and Heisenberg.

According to the Copenhagen interpretation, quantum mechanics only predicts the probabilities that certain outcomes will be realized. The observation affects the outcome, collapsing the wave function on only one of the options. The wave function, in this interpretation, is a superposition of all possible situations, also taking into account the influence of other observers. If you are observing a reality that has already been observed once, the end result will automatically collapse into what has once been perceived. Thus, for example, if there are several observers in a room and one leaves the room, the same reality is still observed, because the wave function has already collapsed and the reality no longer changes. If, on the other hand, there is no observation, there is no reality, the elementary particles don't exist outside of observation. Their properties are determined only as a result of observation.

Increasingly, it seems that ultimately, the consciousness of the observer – the person who observes the result of the measurement – "collapses the wave function" into a certain state, one of the possible options. The research results seem to support the importance of consciousness in the collapse of the wave function. More and more researchers have come to this conclusion. Where the observer focuses their attention has importance for the research results. This explanation of the connection between the collapse of the wave function and consciousness is also called the interpretation of John von Neumann and Wigner. According to von Neumann, we do not observe quantum objects, but "waves of possibility."

The role of consciousness in collapsing the wave function brings a mental, or one could say spiritual, aspect to physics. The role of the human mind needs to be understood. The observation includes the interaction between the object to be observed – thus the material world – and the observer's mind, consciousness – thus the immaterial, spiritual world.

If we assume that consciousness has a role in collapsing the wave function, we arrive at these questions: *Is consciousness needed to observe and collapse the wave function? Can a machine or matter in general collapse the wave function?* There is always a human being at some point observing, at least the result of the experiment. Based on the delayed double-slit experiment we know that observing in itself doesn't collapse the wave function but rather reading the results does. Maybe we need to approach the questions based on Bernardo Kastrup's interpretation and conclude that matter is actually consciousness that has been collapsed, and it thus doesn't have an effect on the wave function?

However, scholars don't agree on the role of consciousness in collapsing the wave function. In Bohm's interpretation, also called the de Broglie-Bohm theory, the wave function includes all the possible states and also takes into account the possibility that the wave function isn't observed, thus not measured. Bohm's causal interpretation is a deterministic and objective approach to quantum mechanics. All the particles have their determined states and they are guided by the wave function as if riding on a guiding wave. Thus, they always include the wave-like nature and their movement is determined. Sometimes the de Broglie-Bohm theory is called the 'pilot wave' theory.

In several later interpretations of quantum physics like the many worlds interpretation, stochastic interpretation and decoherence, scholars have sought a model that would also fit into the ideas of quantum physics. Many of these interpretations include such assumptions as determinism, objectivity and reductionism. The most significant aspect of all of these is the role of the observer. Are they objective observers or subjective influencers?

Currently, physicists Henry Stapp, Menas Kefatos, Roger Penrose and Carlo Rovelli have continued the work on the interpretations of quantum physics. Newer interpretations bring stronger support to the role of consciousness in collapsing the wave function and also indeterminism. For example, Radin *et al.* have studied the effect of consciousness on the results of the double-slit experiment. In the experiment, light behaves like a wave when it is not observed and like a particle when it is observed. I have explained the double-slit experiment in more detail in my book *From Quantum Physics to Energy Healing*. The results of the series of studies carried out by Radin *et al.* support the role of consciousness in our physical reality.

As a conclusion from the many interpretations of quantum physics, one might say that a consensus has not been reached and the discussion is still continuing. Maybe the problem is the fact that all these interpretations, even the most conservative ones, require a revolution in worldview. Maybe it is only now, over a hundred years after the birth of quantum physics, that we are ready to make these changes? Quantum physicist Amit Goswami emphasizes the importance of quantum physics in saying that, if we truly wish to understand our universe, we have to search for the answers from quantum physics instead of through a mechanistic-materialistic approach.

So, do these theories mean that observing something simultaneously creates it? This seems to be the case, if we try to draw conclusions about the role of consciousness and its effect on the results of the experiments. This raises the familiar philosophical question: "When a tree falls in the forest, and nobody is listening, does it make a sound?" Answers are typically divided into two categories: those who think the sound waves travel anyway and it doesn't matter if someone is listening or not, and those who think a sound requires a listener. According to classical physics, a pressure wave is created, but not sound, because in fact sound is created only as the experience of the observer. A sound wave is just a change of pressure in the air. George Berkeley, who is also sometimes presented as the earliest person to ask this question, answers based on subjective idealism that there is no sound, because what is not observed, cannot be real.

Is it thus, also the case that if we weren't here to observe, there wouldn't be the whole universe – that is, reality? If consciousness collapses and even creates matter, how would the world exist without a conscious observer? Or is there an all-encompassing consciousness which creates everything – what Plato spoke of as Form or Idea and Christianity as God?

Johanna Blomqvist

Does quantum physics describe the true reality?

"Quantum" is one of the sexiest words today. "Quantum" and the terminology of quantum physics are widely used outside of scientific research in contexts that have almost nothing to do with quantum physics. "Quantum" is often used to emphasize the importance of an issue or its specific, even revolutionary, nature.

While the general public has embraced the term "quantum," meanwhile in the scientific world quantum physics and the use of its terms is increasingly being viewed with caution. This attitude is well described by the founders of PEAR (Princeton Engineering Anomalies Research) laboratory, Robert Jahn and Brenda Dunne, in their 2011 article in *EdgeScience Magazine*. They discuss how terms of quantum physics are often used to emphasize subtleties and the need for alternative perspectives. Unfortunately, they point out, the wide use of the vocabulary of quantum physics can easily have the exact opposite effect and should therefore be used judiciously. As quantum physics isn't fully understood and it includes a lot of interpretation, conclusions are often drawn that are not based on facts. Jahn and Dunne also remind us that quantum physics, like all the other theories of science as well, are only creations of humans aimed at interpreting observations and experimental data to formalize objective representations. As Albert Einstein aptly stated:

> Concepts which have proved to be useful in ordering things easily acquire such an authority over us that we forget their human origin and accept them as invariable.

However, quantum physics, along with the theory of relativity, is the most revolutionary theory ever developed by humankind. All the hypotheses of quantum physics have been experimentally verified one by one, even though there is no consensus on the interpretation of the theory. Quantum physics is, however, only a creation of humans, only one attempt to understand reality. It doesn't describe reality independent of observations on a quantum level, but only our knowledge of that assumed reality. It gives only probability predictions for certain observations we experience.

We can't say that even on a macro level physics describes an independent reality. Although in science objective reality is sought, human consciousness is always needed to observe and interpret the observations. We can describe reality only as accurately as we can with our own perceptual ability.

Can quantum physics reach what reality truly is? No, at least not where single events are concerned. That is because quantum theory can only give probabilities, and not results for separate, single events. Causality, the cause and effect relation, doesn't work in the same way in quantum physics as it seems to work in everyday life. If, however, we have a set of measurement results, conclusions can be drawn. Statistical causality is then valid. Statistical causality in fact describes the change in a viewpoint on reality, when we move from classical physics to quantum physics. We can't for example predict the location of a certain particle, because the accuracy is defined by the uncertainty principle, as described by Werner Heisenberg. We can only define certain probabilities within which a particle can be found from a certain location. In a similar way the particle's energy and time cannot be defined accurately simultaneously. Heisenberg's uncertainty principle defines the limits: Information more accurate than this cannot be obtained. The concept of deterministic causality that has been characteristic of scientific thinking from the 17th century until today, should thus be abandoned. The importance of this hasn't been very widely understood, and this isn't reflected in our common ways of thinking.

We used to think that all events have a cause that can be shown. We have learned this causality, the cause and effect relation, and it is also a part of materialistic thinking. From modern physics we have learned that all laws are statistical, and we, thus, can't explain single events with these laws. "Statistical" means that we can describe the behavior of large datasets, but in the case of single events we are not able to give unambiguous answers.

One important fact needs to be mentioned, too. The laws of physics that apply on the particle level are more general than the laws of the macro level. They apply to both micro and macro levels. The laws of the macro level, instead, give erroneous answers if they are applied on the particle level. Therefore, what has been found relevant at the atomic level needs to be considered more widely than when studying the phenomena only of the particle level. Classical physics would seem to be only a special case of quantum physics.

From objectivity to subjectivity

Maybe our starting point to study observation has been wrong? What if we don't assume the materialistic world as primary, as we so easily do? As an idealist, you have to accept the fact that when you are observing something, in practice you change the physical object when you are studying it. That requires a huge shift in thinking compared to materialism. We are not separate, unconnected parts in a world, but instead active influencers and even creators. Change in this direction already seems to be in progress. For example, a growing number of scholars have started to use the first person singular or plural in scientific articles, instead of an objective third-person or non-subject approach; that is, they are saying, "I measured" or "we observed," "we conclude" and so on. Nowhere in science can the effect of an observer be avoided. It is impossible for us to create a closed environment for the study of a certain phenomenon, so the observer must always be taken into account as well as the influence of all those involved in the study on the results. The human is a psycho-physical entity. All this needs to be taken into account in everyday life as well.

The observer effect would seem to be a more important part of the experimental set-up than we have assumed.

BENGSTON'S MICE

In my book *From Quantum Physics to Energy Healing,* I wrote about William Bengston's energy healing studies. Bengston has conducted (as of March 2021) 18 controlled studies in an attempt to understand the healing of mice from certain extremely active forms of mammary cancer. The mammary cancer under study has been very widely used, with over 2,000 experiments recorded, with the death rate of 100%. All the mice studied have died between days 14 and 27 when they have been injected with this cancer type. The mice were treated with the hands-on healing technique developed by Bengston and based on his own experience of overcoming a chronic condition with hands-on healing. All mice were treated 30–60 minutes daily, until they were either cured or dead. In Bengston's experiments over 90% of the mice treated were cured for the first time from these cancer forms known to be deadly.

Bengston has achieved some pretty interesting findings in these experiments. He has, for example, found out that mice that are part of the experiment are cured, even if the healers don't know which mice are among the ones that are being treated. It is enough that this has been decided when the experiment is being planned.

Bengston has also noticed that the mice in the control groups also seem to be cured, if they are located nearby, for example in the same building as the mice being treated. Mice were also cured if the healers visited the place where the mice of the control group were kept. It was preferable to take the mice of the control group to another city, far from the mice being treated and the healers, as well. Then the mice of the control group were not cured. Bengston calls this phenomenon "resonance bonding" and states that it is really difficult to separate groups from each other, as they often seem to have some kind of a connection, at least through the planner of the experiment. This phenomenon could have a larger effect than we think. Could the placebo  effect be a kind of resonance bonding? Bengston has also noticed that when the mice once cured from a certain cancer-type were re-injected, they no longer got the same cancer-type. This seems to suggest they developed immunity.

The research series is in many ways revolutionary, not least because of the method, energy healing, that is not understood by the prevailing materialistic thinking.

There is a common belief in the natural sciences that there exists an independent objective reality. According to Einstein, this is only assumed, even though it cannot be proved. The developers of quantum physics, Bohr, Heisenberg, Born and Pauli also believed in the existence of this kind of an independent reality, at least in the beginning. The starting point for quantum physics was that we can only trust experiments and we shouldn't assume anything about reality. Pauli especially ended up concluding that reality has to be psycho-physical. Empirical reality must be psycho-physical, because it is observed by humans. Because natural laws seem to be statistical and independent, the "true" reality has to have both rational and irrational features that resemble the way the human psyche works.

According to Bohr, the role of the human is essential not only in quantum physics but also in the other significant theory of modern physics, the theory of relativity. Space and time cannot be separated from the observer. Observations are dependent on the observer and their location. Bohr sees the observer having a focal role in descriptions of the theories of both relativity and quantum physics. The conclusion is that we need to renew our prevailing assumptions about physical reality. We can't avoid the fact that we have to take into consideration the physical issues and question objectivity in physics. Bohr was highly respected among scholars and the effect of his emphasis on materialistic thinking has been significant. Bohr tried to stay out of the discussions and of the attempts to merge the ideas of quantum physics with Eastern philosophies and Vedanta. He wanted to stay away from unnecessary mystification – and also metaphysics. However, it tells us something about Bohr's thoughts that when he was awarded a Danish Order of the Elephant to honor his work, he chose for his coat of arms the taijitu (Yin-Yang) symbol, with the text "*Opposites are complementary*."

Shifting our mindset from objectivity to subjectivity is a challenge. Objective information can be said to be impartial, but there is no such guarantee about the truthfulness of the subjective. You can trust the information only if you consider its source to be truthful.

Even the developers of quantum physics at the beginning of the last century saw the role of the subjective observer and its consideration as important, and even self-evident. During the last centuries attention has been on understanding the properties of matter, and we now understand it rather well. Matter, experience and consciousness would seem to have a connection. We shouldn't consider them as separate, but instead by studying matter we learn more about consciousness, ourselves and reality.

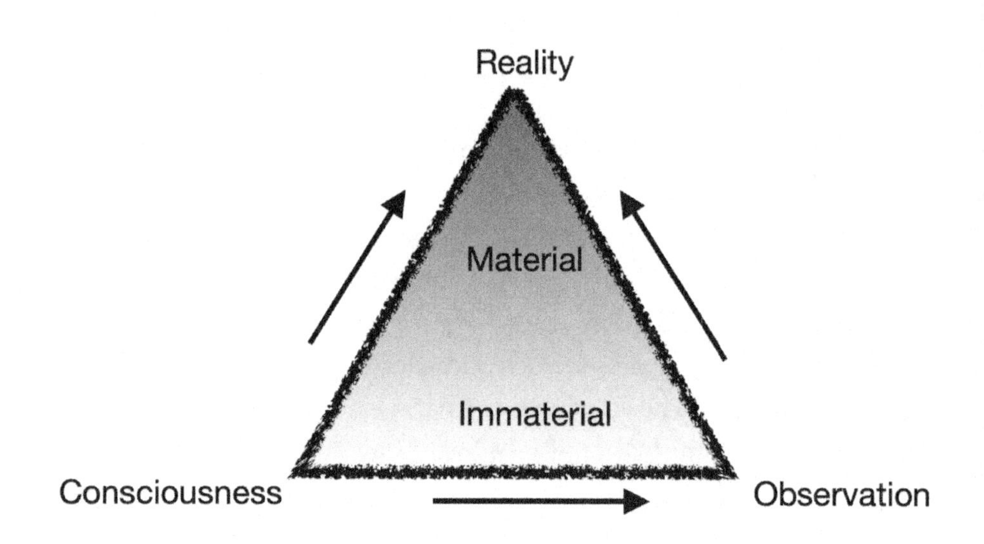

FIGURE 9. CONSCIOUSNESS - OBSERVATION - REALITY.

The existence of matter cannot be explained separately or without its subjective consideration in consciousness. We don't have proof that matter would exist without consciousness, as observation always requires consciousness. Maybe matter is only a form of consciousness? Just as water turns solid at the freezing point, could matter be consciousness solidified at the point of observation?

Philosopher Bertrand Russell says: "*We know nothing about the intrinsic quality of physical events, except when these are mental events that we directly experience.*"

The observer creates the state of the particle; before observation it doesn't even exist. We have to change our thinking and consider consciousness as one of the fundamental quantities, like other quantities in physics that are considered as fundamental, such as gravity or the speed of light.

Observation changes reality and even creates the reality we observe.

CHAPTER 6
QUANTUM REALITY

The opposite of a correct statement is a false statement. But the opposite of a profound truth may well be another profound truth.

—Niels Bohr

If you are not completely confused by quantum mechanics, you do not understand it.

—John Wheeler

I have always liked drawing and painting. Earlier, I even thought of doing it professionally. When you paint, you can never be completely sure of the end result. Each artist has their own perspective and creates a different-looking version, their own interpretation, even of the same object. At a younger age, my favorite artist was Salvador Dalí, for his surreal work. *Surrealism* literally means "over-realism"; it describes reality, but in its own way, it tries to go beyond the usual thinking and boundaries. Maybe that's what engaged me – a different perspective to view the world and break boundaries. Everything is not what it seems to be at first sight. Dalí's melting pocket watches in "The Persistence of Memory" describe perfectly what I pondered, and as a teenager it was comforting to know that you were not alone with your thoughts. All the pocket watches seem to point to a different time, so how can you tell what is the right time? There is peace and stability in the painting but also anxiety. Ants seem to dig themselves into one watch, as if trying to find the right time, the true reality. The same theme about understanding reality and cutting it to pieces continues in the work "Galatea of the Spheres," which represents Dalí's wife Gala using spheres as an atomic model; in it the spheres appear to continue to infinity and disappear into the horizon. Some of the balls seem to be moving, vibrating. All this together depicts her character as both strong and sensitive and, simultaneously, as if it could break up into parts at any moment. Dalí himself said the painting depicts the unity of the universe. He knew how to capture perfectly in his paintings the moment that contains everything essential.

The effect of quantum physics could be seen in Dalí's work. As an aesthetic movement, Surrealism took place during the same period as the birth of quantum physics, in the early 20th century. Even today, over a hundred years after its inception, quantum theory is the most successful theory that we currently have. The applications of quantum physics – computers, TV, internet and so on – have already changed our world, even though our thinking hasn't changed in step with it. Can we learn a new way of thinking? Actually, the change is already ongoing and a new paradigm is dawning based on the ideas of quantum physics.

Quantum physics offers fundamental answers to ontological questions, that is, it tries to give answers about the nature of reality. In this chapter, I face a challenging task. Without clinging to the web of multiple interpretations of quantum physics, I try to put together what kind of view on reality it actually provides. What is reality according to quantum physics?

We are one

Our body consists of cells, cells consist of molecules and molecules of atoms. The interactions between atoms can be described using quantum mechanics. Atoms vibrate, rotate and radiate energy, each in their own way. We are thus all, at the particle level, only energy and vibrations. The whole universe is in fact a network of interconnected energy clusters. Everything is entangled with everything else through energy, and thus, we are all connected with each other. Fundamentally, we are one and the same energy. We are not limited to the physical body, which we experience as separate. We are much more than that.

According to quantum physics, then, we are all one and the same vibrating energy on a particle level. It is even impossible to say where I end and someone else begins. On a particle level we are one, and there is no separateness.

Based on these ideas, it is easy to accept that how I treat others comes back to myself as well. According to quantum physics, there is only one great unity.

***

I am writing this book in a cafe. My iPad is in front of me and in the background I hear "Moon River" playing. There is a really relaxed, easygoing feeling. *"Two drifters, off to see the world ... There's such a lot of world to see,"* the song says.

It is unbelievable how much the world has changed in only 10 or 20 years! I remember so well the day I defended my doctoral thesis work, almost 20 years ago. The invitations to participate in the doctoral defense were sent by mail ("snail mail") to my collaborators and relatives a week before the event. The advertisement of my doctoral dissertation was published in the (paper) journal of the university – which was read more than the website. A box of printed copies of my thesis had also been brought to me, although at that time in the spring of 2001 my thesis was among the first in the University of Helsinki to be made available via the internet (a link to my dissertation can be found in the references). When the doctoral defense event began, I gave a lecture using an overhead projector. I had carefully prepared my presentation and written the most important points on transparency sheets. There were hardly any laptops yet available, at least not very light or inexpensive ones. Additionally, I had a stack of files, in which, if necessary, I would look for an answer if the opponent of my dissertation asked too difficult a question. Unfortunately, I forgot our new digital camera, a technology that had just started to become more common, at home. I had my cell phone, but it didn't have a camera.

In fact, applications of quantum physics have made it possible for us today to be almost constantly connected to each other via the internet and mobile phones, as one network. We are one through devices, but not yet at the level of the mind. In a way, we have already begun to live in the way quantum physics implies: where we are all one.

***

Niels Bohr states: "*Everything we call real is made of things that cannot be regarded as real.*"

In fact, the material reality now parallels the reality we perceive at the particle level. Which one is more real: a material table that I perceive with the senses, or an energy table that is observed at the particle level? Or our body compared to our energy body? In addition, there are other ways of perceiving reality that are not usually addressed in science, such as intuition. Reality looks different from different levels and from different perspectives.

Professor Meinard Kuhlmann explains the unreality of particles by saying that interactions and properties can be more fundamental than the substance itself. For example, at the macro level, features such as the brown color of the table and the feel of a shiny surface may be more real than the object itself. Plato would certainly have agreed with this as well. Maybe all that exists is just the vibration of particles? Mere information that looks different from different perspectives.

Actually, quantum mechanics describes only interactions, for example what happens when two particles interact with each other. Thus, reality in quantum physics only means interactions. The behavior of particles can only be clarified by studying the interactions: Reality is how others see you.

Quantum physics doesn't include details on the reasons, on why a certain reality is selected. Nor does it tell us where the particle was before the observation. The direction of time doesn't really even matter. In fact, quantum physics doesn't tell you how things really are; it tells you what happens in the interaction, for example when two particles encounter each other. In quantum physics, reality is only visible in interactions, that is, when particles meet and when the observer observes the event. The same principles that govern at the particle level govern everything in our universe. We are also part of this whole. The universe is interactive – interactions are an important part of it, even a constitutive part of it.

Niels Bohr also states: *"Isolated material particles are abstractions, their properties being definable and observable only through their interaction with other systems."*

Reality fades when described accurately

Particles behave in a different way at the particle level than objects at the macro level. For example, when determining the location of a particle, the act of measuring simultaneously changes the momentum and velocity of the particle, just as measuring with a thermometer changes the temperature of the system being measured. The change in velocity is inversely proportional to the accuracy of the measurement of the particle location. Thus, the more accurately the location of a particle is determined, the less certain the momentum of the particle is. The location and momentum are complementary quantities, meaning they cannot be determined accurately at the same time, nor can energy and time. The more accurately one can be determined, the less accurate the information about the other is. This phenomenon is known as the Heisenberg uncertainty principle, and it gives the limits of measurement accuracy. The principle also determines how a particle behaves when one of the quantities is changed. For example, if a particle is brought into a narrow space and the inaccuracy of its location decreases, its momentum and velocity forcibly increase due to the uncertainty principle.

Quantum physics revealed a new feature characteristic of reality: It fades if you try to describe it accurately. There are no measurement devices that could help to reveal everything about particles, and the most essential features always seem to remain unanswered. According to Bohr, the uncertainty in describing the details is not a sign of the imperfection of the theory or the effect of measurement. Instead, it reveals a new feature of reality that is incompatible with the deterministic ideas of classical physics. It seems that the smaller the scale, the closer one moves to consciousness, information, and non-locality.

Reality is irrational

Particles seem to work in co-operation. It's impossible to predict the behavior of a single particle, but their common behavior can be predicted. We can, for example, illustrate a probability distribution and use it to predict where the particle will most likely travel. However, a single particle can travel anywhere freely; that is, the deterministic causality of classical physics does not hold. The path of the particle is not known in advance. At the particle level, deterministic causality must be replaced by a more general concept of causality, statistical causality. At the particle level, there are laws of probability that are statistical in nature, that is, they do not apply to separate events but to large groups. It is therefore, in principle, impossible to describe individual events.

There is an irrational aspect of reality, something that we cannot explain based on the cause-effect understanding we have learned.

Thus, single incidents involve freedom. This was considered by Pauli to be the most important philosophical teaching of quantum mechanics. It seems that particles all have access to the same information that collectively controls their behavior. Individual particles have the freedom to choose, within certain limits.

However, it is not easy to let go of causality, which has been the basis of scientific explanations since the days of Galileo and Newton. Causality underlies our prevailing view of materialistic reality. Even for the creators of quantum mechanics, the statistical nature of particle-level reality was a difficult problem. In the 1950s, Born and Heisenberg described how quantum mechanics does not describe the atomic world itself, but our knowledge of  this world. Pauli emphasized that there are irrational features in reality: A complete description of particle-level phenomena is impossible, but with the help of quantum mechanics it is possible to obtain statistical descriptions of the particle-level world. Bohr presented it so that we cannot describe individual phenomena in detail, but the explanations are reliable if we study a large number of similar atomic phenomena.

Like statistical causality, complementarity is irrational as well. The wave-particle dualism that underlies quantum physics, in which two mutually exclusive descriptions are used to describe atomic systems, represents opposite, complementary, ways of describing the same reality.

In fact, the complementarity of reality actually belongs to metaphysics. Bohr, who rejected metaphysics, refused to discuss the concept of reality at all. Pauli emphasized that it is impossible to draw a strict line between physics and metaphysics and the attempt to do so leads to a dangerous one-sidedness.

However, all this controversy does not negate the fact that two mutually exclusive descriptions are needed to describe the same reality. Reality is irrational and we cannot reach it using only rationality.

Reality is entangled

Entanglement refers to how there is still a connection between two particles that are far apart, even on opposite sides of the earth: The state of one particle contains information on the state of the other particle. When one is affected, there is instantly a change in the other. Entanglement can occur for particles as well as for groups of particles. The phenomenon is also visible immediately.

Entanglement was described by Schrödinger in the 1920s. In practice, it means contact or effect from a distance, without any known means of interaction. Einstein called the phenomenon "spooky action at a distance" (*Spukhafte Fernwirkung*, in German), because the interaction between particles shouldn't be possible. The phenomenon is non-local, independent of the location. Einstein's opinion was that quantum physics was imperfect in these respects. Other scholars, who tried to find a logical, deterministic explanation for the phenomenon, thought so too. Entanglement was, however, experimentally verified in the 1970s–1980s. In 2011, the scholars of Niels Bohr Institute and Max Planck Institute even noted entanglement in an experiment for two clouds of cesium both containing two trillion atoms (10^{12}). Entanglement is a very sensitive phenomenon, but in their experiment the entanglement between clouds was sustained for an entire hour using special technology.

Whether there is a limit to how large a system entanglement may exist in is still unknown. The challenge is now to be able to build a quantum computer based on entanglement, and to understand the phenomenon better, since some scholars think entanglement could help us understand space and time and connect to the theory of relativity. Might entanglement turn out to be the connection between quantum mechanics and the theory of relativity?

Einstein suggested there must be hidden variables that would explain entanglement. In the 1960s, physicist John Bell presented a test for these kind of hidden variables, which he based on the following three assumptions:

1. Realism – Objects have their properties, whether or not we observe them.
2. Locality – There is no interaction that would require a signal to move faster than light.
3. Freedom of choice – Physicists can freely plan their measurements and are not controlled by any hidden variables.

The assumptions can be tested using experiments on entanglement. If the experiments show that nature relies on – or behaves according to – these assumptions, we live in a world that can be described using classical physics, and the hidden variables only create an illusion of quantum entanglement. If the experiments show that nature does not rely on these, quantum entanglement is real.

The experiments have shown that when particles are entangled, the results of measurements are statistically more correlated than in a classical system, and thus contradict Bell's assumptions. The experimental results can be explained best if the demand for realism and locality are discarded.

According to Bell, the results can be explained only by an absolute determinism:

> Suppose the world is super-deterministic, with not just inanimate nature running on behind-the-scenes clockwork, but with our behavior, including our belief that we are free to choose to do one experiment rather than another, absolutely predetermined, including the 'decision' by the experimenter to carry out one set of measurements rather than another, the difficulty disappears. There is no need for a

> faster-than-light signal to tell particle A what measurement has been carried out on particle B, because the universe, including particle A, already 'knows' what that measurement, and its outcome, will be.

Similarly, the flow of information is possible if it is assumed that all information is in consciousness or in an all-pervading field to which we are constantly connected. If entanglement is examined through the lens of idealism, would the phenomenon perhaps be more comprehensible? Maybe entanglement is due to the fact that matter emanates from a lower level, from a smaller scale? The smaller the scale, the more the material seems to be information?

Entanglement also highlights the importance of interaction. In some studies carried out on single particles, such as that of Blasiak *et al.*, it was discovered that at least some of the phenomena can be explained based on classical laws. Their suggestion is that, in fact, quantum phenomena would actually affect multi-particle systems. Moreva *et al.* suggest the entanglement of particles also leads to the appearance of time.

There is a mental side to reality

Consciousness has no place in Newton's classical mechanics. The theory of relativity does not include consciousness, although the observer plays a key role in it. Quantum physics, instead, suggests that consciousness affects the material world, and that there is a mental aspect to natural sciences. There is still no consensus on this, more than a hundred years after the birth of quantum physics. The question of the role of consciousness represents a revolutionary change in thinking for which several interpretations of quantum physics have sought to find an answer. "Spirituality" is a word that has not been salient in the philosophy of science, either, but it has been legible there, if only between the lines. Reality is both material and mental, and this connection must be explained if we want answers and an understanding of what reality is. First, however, this connection must also be accepted in science.

There is a mental aspect to reality that doesn't belong to the version of material reality the natural sciences currently describe. This mental, or spiritual, side, however, essentially affects how we describe the world of matter. As we have seen, materialism alone is an inadequate model to describe reality. Many developers and interpreters of quantum mechanics have stated this, but the claim has often been rejected, since it is interpreted to mean we have to let go of the notion of objective and rational reality.

Bohr's view was that considering a mental aspect would allow for subjectivity, which has no place in objective science. In the article *Atomphysik und Philosophie. Kausalität und Komplementarität, 1958,* Bohr states:

> Crucially, the proper expansion of our conceptualization never involves the involvement of the observing subject, which would prevent unambiguous descriptions of experiences.

The outsize influence of Bohr and Einstein, who couldn't agree with some of the features of the Copenhagen interpretation, is apparent in the fact that the possible effect of the observing subject and psychic phenomena is

generally excluded from consideration in quantum theory. However, many physicists have disagreed on this point, including Pauli and a growing number of scientists today. Pauli's view was that the interplay of the "mental world" and the "world of matter" is the biggest problem in the natural sciences, and it still is.

***

Quantum theory is the most successful current theory of science: It is functional, consistent and accurate in describing the phenomena of the particle world. There is no doubt that it gives correct predictions, as evidenced by several modern applications.

For over a century now, scientists have sought a materialistic interpretation for quantum physics emphasizing scientific realism and have even completely ignored interpretation of the theory as outside the scope of the job of physicists.

Quantum physics is not limited to the particle level, because the same principles govern everything in our world. In the following chapters, I will explore whether the view on reality that quantum physics offers is actually already visible on the everyday level, but usually goes unnoticed – or is not understood:

- According to quantum physics, we are one and on a continuum with our environment. Does this mean that we can also influence physical reality?
- In quantum physics, reality is irrational: Single incidents involve freedom, and causality does not apply. Do we, thus, have free will? Can the consequence also precede the cause at the macro level? What about the phenomenon of synchronicity; is this an indication that the cause-and-effect relationship is not working?
- Reality is also complementary, in that opposites do not exclude each other but together form a whole. Reality is both physical and mental, and there are phenomena that are independent of time and place. Is time an illusion? Can science and spirituality be combined?

CHAPTER 7
CAN WE AFFECT PHYSICAL REALITY?

To study the abnormal is the best way of understanding the normal.

—William James

Reality is built out of thought, and our every thought begins to create reality.

—Edgar Cayce

I have a lamp in my home that randomly selects the color it shows from eight different options. The randomness in the lamp is realized by means of a random number generator, the operation of which is based on the tunneling phenomenon of quantum mechanics, where electrons can randomly tunnel through a potential energy wall to the other side. I did a small test using the lamp. I wrote down 25 predictions about which of the eight possible colors I wished the lamp to show. Then I did 25 tests. In each test, I focused my mind on the color I had chosen. The first three tests were promising – all correct! However, that seemed to be only beginner's luck, since after that the lamp started playing with me. At least, that's what it seemed to be doing. When I wanted a purple color, for almost five minutes it continued to flash purple light, but then turned to its opposite color, yellow. This was also the case with my other favorite color, red. After five minutes of flashing, the result was green. The end result in my small experiment was that 9 out of 25 were correct, which is a rather good result. The probability for this kind of a result occurring by chance would be 1 in 10,000!

Was this, thus, a proof that it is possible to influence a physical device by thoughts?

Talking about things in theory is a completely different experience than seeing them concretely in practice. If it is possible to prove that we can influence physical reality with our thoughts, feelings, or in general, the consequences would be revolutionary. That would mean we should change our perception of the world and how things happen. It would also mean what we *think* about ourselves or other people really would matter.

Psychically influencing physical reality has been extensively studied. Instead of "influencing physical reality," studies often refer to "non-local" influencing, in other words, influencing that happens at a distance. In addition to non-local influencing, anomalous interaction or, for example, human-machine interaction are also discussed. In parapsychology, influencing physical reality is called psychokinesis (PK), which literally means movement (*kinesis*) using your mind (*psyche*).

Human-machine interaction

One of the longest-running projects on the influence of the mind on physical reality is the research program at the Princeton Engineering Anomalies Research (PEAR) laboratory at Princeton University, conducted from 1979 to 2007. The purpose of Robert Jahn, Dean of Princeton University and Brenda Dunne, Head of Laboratory, was to systematically study the possibility of the human mind, either consciously or unconsciously, influencing physical devices and to study remote perception. In the former project, the intention-induced changes in various randomized physical devices, such as random number generators, were studied; the latter examined the ability of volunteers to describe geographical locations, independent of time and place, and developed analytical methods to measure the results obtained. These results can be found in more detail in several publications on the subject; only some of the main points of the results are presented below.

The randomness was delivered in PEAR studies using random number/event generators, (RNG/REG), that usually randomly produce zeros and ones. There are different kinds of random number generators, either based on algorithms that create seemingly random number sequences or based on physical quantum phenomena that actually generate random number sequences. The true random number generators, which were also used in the PEAR program (and which is in my lamp as well), are based on quantum world processes such as radioactive decay or electron tunneling, where the electron tunnels completely randomly, while producing a small voltage. This is a coin toss at the quantum level, where both zero and one have the same probability.

The participants in the study were asked to influence the data – zeros, and ones – produced by the random number generator using only their minds. For example, the participant created in their mind the intention that the result would more likely be number one than zero. Only small variations were observed in the mean distributions of data collected from human-machine studies in the PEAR laboratory. The single measurement events were not individually anomalous, but the effect achieved in millions of experiments performed together proved to be statistically very significant. The results cannot be explained by chance. The probability that similar results would be obtained by chance was about 1 in 15,000.

A similar phenomenon was observed in all experiments, regardless of the physical device affected or the process from the micro level to the macro level. The data gathered during the 28 years of the research project provide clear proof that thoughts and emotions affect our physical reality. The data gathered also indicate the connection between immaterial and material can be measured, at least statistically.

In the remote perception experiments of the PEAR laboratory, it was noted that untrained volunteers were able to receive information from remote geographical locations without any well-known means of obtaining information, like normal senses. Information was received independently of time or location. The main goal of the research project wasn't to verify the phenomenon of remote perception, but instead to develop analytical methods to quantify the results. In the remote human-machine interaction experiments significant results were also obtained, which didn't seem to fade as time or distance increased.

An interesting observation was made in the experiment when volunteers worked in pairs. The task of the pairs was to form an intention together, a wish regarding how to affect the machine. The effect obtained was, on average, about twice as large as when they tried to affect it individually – as long as the volunteers were of a different gender. Pairs of the same gender weren't able to produce an effect larger than that of chance, even if they were able to separately produce a significant effect. If the pairs of different genders were also emotionally bonded with each other, for example a married couple, their average effect on the results was almost seven times larger than separately.

Also, a general comment about the results: When the person repeated the experiments, the first series were always the most successful, with the strongest effects. This seemed to be a replicable pattern that was well beyond what could be expected based on chance. They, however, experienced the most uncertainty during the first series and first attempts. In the second series, when the person already had some kind of a hunch about how the experiment worked, they mainly received results that were opposite to their own intention (as I had in my lamp experiment, when the color I wished for was exactly the opposite!). In the next experiments, the result of the earlier experiment was repeated, but to a lesser extent than at the beginning. The participants received the best results when they didn't intentionally try to make a change. If there was relaxed feeling, as if they were only playing, the results were better. The participants also experienced that it was less important to maintain the intention than it was to make an emotional bond to the task in question.

CHICKS AND ROBOT "MOTHER"

In one experiment by René Peoc'h, newly hatched chicks were imprinted on a randomly driven robot. The direction of "Mother's" movement was defined by a random number generator, and thus all directions were as probable. When the chicks were separated from their "mother" by being confined in a cage at one end of the robot's range of activity, the robot, which was supposed to move randomly, spent a significantly disproportionate amount of time in that corner where the chicks' cage was! After all, the robot should have spent the same amount of time all over the area. Chicks that were emotionally bonded to their robot "mother" seemed to be able to affect the behavior of a robot's random process. Besides humans, animals are thus also able to produce significant statistical changes in machines.

PHILODENDRON AND THE LIGHT-REGULATING COMPUTER

In another experiment, it was noted that plants also have the ability to affect devices. In the experiment, a Philodendron was put in a darkened space that had an adjustable grille on its roof. When the plant needed more light, it had to affect the regulating mechanism, which opened the hatch on the roof further. There were remarkable results in the first few days, when the plant was able to affect the mechanism and receive more light. The days after that were totally different, and the plant didn't get much light. On the day after that, the computer that regulated the mechanism suddenly broke. When the experiment was studied more thoroughly, it was discovered that the mechanism had a random number generator that was based on algorithms, so that it sometimes got a large number as a seed number and occasionally a small number, and based on that, formed a series of random numbers. The scholars of the experiment suspected that affecting a random system like this must be really difficult. The plant therefore may have caused the computer to break down.

The PEAR laboratory also gave rise to the Global Consciousness project, which studied the effect of humans on the operation of random number generators worldwide. The project found that when a group of people focused their attention on something in common, the data produced by random number generators located around the globe were no longer so random. Examples of such anomalies in measurements have accumulated over the years, such as the tsunami in the Indian Ocean on December 26, 2004; September 11, 2001; and the death and funeral of Princess Diana in August and September 1997; as well as several worldwide meditation and praying events. Random number generators began to deviate significantly from random a few hours before these events. The data of 9/11, for example, have been reviewed and analyzed with particular care, and analysts have found the deviation to continue for a couple of days, with the most critical data analysts commenting that the deviation is only marginal compared to the usual. Researchers of the Global Consciousness project urge us to look at the data as a whole. In individual cases, the deviations are small, but when considered together, they are all in line and therefore statistically significant. The project is still ongoing, currently under the IONS (Institute of Noetic Sciences), while the PEAR laboratory ceased operations in 2007 after Robert Jahn retired.

One might ask: If humans focus on the same target, why can the changing of the focus be seen in random number generators? What physics is beneath all this? However, the approach implied by these questions might be erroneous. We ask these questions because our thinking is so based on materialism, and we assume that only the data produced by the random event generators change. The situation is different if we assume we live in a universe where everything is conscious and matter somehow emanates from consciousness. If something happens in collective consciousness, and our attention suddenly focuses on a certain common object, the localized consciousness also becomes focused and coherent. Then, the matter arising from consciousness also changes, when attention is no longer on millions of different objects. When consciousness is localized, the physical world is also organized differently. Not only do the data produced by the random event generators change, but the whole physical world changes as well due to our consciousness. Our thoughts and emotions have a huge effect!

Psychokinesis

Psychokinesis (PK) (from Greek *psykhe* mind, soul, spirit and *kinesis*, motion, movement) can be divided to either macro-PK or micro-PK, depending on whether one examines phenomena that are observable with the naked eye, like bending metal or moving a table, or phenomena observed by way of statistics, for example a phenomenon due to a random operation of an electrical device. PK includes phenomena in which something happens unexpectedly in physical devices that is thought to be the effect of the mind, such as the sudden stopping of a dead person's clock at the time of their death.

Often, PK phenomena can be explained only by chance. PK has been studied less than ESP (Extra Sensory Perception) since compared to ESP these kinds of phenomena are reported far less. One of the first comprehensive PK studies were done by Louise Rhine, who gathered data on phenomena in the field of parapsychology at Duke University in the 1960s. Over 10,000 cases of the data were ESP phenomena and only 178 PK cases. Louise and J.B. Rhine later established the Rhine Research Center, which studies parapsychological phenomena.

Many may think that psychokinesis is when one tries to move a table or twist a spoon with the mind, and often these kinds of tricks may be explained by optical illusion. However, psychokinesis seems to be a real phenomenon that we have all experienced, but many times the phenomenon is simply ignored due to its ambiguous nature, since the cases are not as clear as those of ESP. Only the most anomalous cases are noticed.

"PK MAN"

In his book *The PK Man*, Jeffery Mishlove discusses Ted Owens, a man who had an exceptional ability to produce massive PK phenomena. Mishlove followed the man for years, documenting events in which Owens caused earthquakes and storms and various meteorological phenomena, and directed volcanic lava and floods. Owens himself explained his abilities by claiming he had extraterrestrial helpers who assisted to make his wishes come true. According to Owens, he only created a picture in his mind of his wish for what would happen and then connected in his mind to this reality, and the wish came true. Thus, in a way, he manifested his wish as reality.

PK seems to be a phenomenon similar to entanglement, where two particles are connected even though they are far apart. Maybe we should try to understand how the connection is formed in the case of PK?

Could the phenomenon also be the same in several documented meditation experiments? By changing the state of consciousness and connecting to an intention, a future state is made to occur. There are several examples of this kind of meditation experiment, for example those in studies by Maharishi Mahesh Yogin and John Hagelin. In one study done in Washington, DC, 4,000 people meditated together and in two months, the number of violent crimes in a particular area fell by 48%. Hagelin is well acquainted with Vedic texts, and he has been developing a Unified Field Theory. In the Global Consciousness project, the effect of meditation on the results was also observed; it was noted that during large meditation events there seems to be a clear statistical change in data. In another example, writer Lynne McTaggart has recently organized extensive intention events, where a large number of people have focused, for example, on bringing peace to a particular region, such as Sri Lanka. Data collected from these events indicate that intention has a positive effect. Even more surprisingly, there also seemed to be positive changes in the participants' own lives, as if they had hoped for help in their own lives.

Can a spoon, then, be bent by the power of the mind? Why would that be impossible? A spoon is usually made of some kind of metal, so at the atomic level it is only a vibration of particles, which it is possible to change. Without taking a stance on psychokinesis, it is true that extra energy makes the atoms of the spoon vibrate faster and energy enables the properties and structure to change. But where is that energy coming from?

In his book, *Autobiography of a Yogi*, Paramahansa Yogananda talks about the astral level, which a yogi with sufficient training could possibly reach. At this level, all wishes come true. Maybe it's something like that? Maybe everything we consider possible will also become possible? And similarly, if we consider something impossible, is it also impossible?

In the 1950s, running a mile (1609.35 m) in less than 4 minutes was considered the absolute limit of human performance. Attempts were made to break this record for years, but when Roger Bannister ran a mile in less than four minutes on May 6, 1954, there suddenly were 4-minute-mile runners in almost every race. It was as if lead weights had been removed from the runners' feet. The current world record time for 1 mile is 3.43.13 minutes, set by Hicham el-Guerrouji on July 7, 1999.

Remote influencing in living systems

Almost everyone has had experiences like thinking of someone, then hearing the phone suddenly ring and finding it was that person calling. We, biological systems, have a connection to each other, and distance doesn't matter. When there are enough anecdotes, together they are a sign of a significant phenomenon. Therefore, it is important to share these stories and make them public. The proof is growing that there is a connection between all of us. The topic has also been studied and published in peer-reviewed journals. We can conclude that aside from affecting machines, we can also non-locally affect each other.

Remote influencing in living systems has also been studied under laboratory conditions. These experiments are called DMILS (Distant Mental Interactions with Living Systems) experiments. Remote healing is one example of DMILS. Remote healing is healing, wishing, meditation or praying, that one or a group of healers performs intentionally from a distance.

BENGSTON'S MICE AND THE EFFECT OF DISTANCE

Earlier, I mentioned William Bengston's energy healing studies. Bengston also studied the effect of distance. In these studies, the distance of healers from the mice varied from beside the mice to almost a thousand kilometers away. The distance didn't seem to have an effect on the results of the experiments. Bengston and Moga noticed similar changes in magnetic fields, whether the healer was beside the healee or far away. Near the healers similar changes were not observed. Bengston's research series is a proof that energy healing and remote energy healing are phenomena that are reproducible and predictable, and also reliable, and even distance doesn't matter.

In addition to remote healing, influencing over a distance has also been examined in many other studies, which have found that the phenomenon is detectable in cells and can be seen in the brain through functional magnetic resonance imaging (fMRI) and electroencephalogram (EEG) measurements. Among other things, it has been found that identical twins experience the same emotions and physical reactions even though they are far apart. Often these may be interpreted as just coincidence.

TWINS MARTA AND SILVIA LANDAU

It is difficult to draw a conclusion from Marta and Silvia Landau's case that the connection between similar experiences were just a coincidence. These Spanish four-year-old twin girls had an incomprehensibly close bond between them: What happened to one was immediately apparent in the other. When Marta burned her hand on the iron while at her grandmother's, Silvia, who was miles away at home, felt severe pain in the same hand and formed a blister similar to her sister's. G. Playfair studied the twins with his group and reported on how Marta's reflexes were studied by tapping the knee, and at the same time Silvia's leg began to swing, even though the twins were in different rooms. The same continued in the other experiments: As Marta smelled perfume, Silvia covered her nose at the same time. As a light was shone in Marta's eyes, Silvia blinked, her eyes dripping. The girls had a very strong connection.

Similar experiences of connection are known to occur especially in situations where a close family member experiences something unexpectedly, such as having an accident or even dying. You may get the feeling that something has happened, sometimes even bodily sensations.

In Jacobo Grinberg-Zylberbaum's studies a correlation was also found in the case of people unknown to each other. Grinberg-Zylberbaum's measurements were published in the reputable *Physics Essays and International Journal of Neuroscience,* encouraging more researchers to explore the subject.

Are these cases examples of the possibility that the resonance bonding suggested by Bengston could be possible in everyday life? Maybe we humans can also form a similar system? Information would seem to flow mentally. Maybe there exists an information field where all the information is, and sometimes we're more closely connected to that information? We humans also seem to have this kind of a bond with each other, which is especially evident in some situations, just like birds flying as one in flocks or fish swimming in schools.

EMOTO'S ICE CRYSTAL AND RICE EXPERIMENTS

Masaru Emoto studied the effect of human consciousness on molecular structures of water. The effect of thoughts on water was studied by crystallizing the water and studying the differences between the ice crystals. It has been repeatedly observed that positive thoughts produce symmetrical, well-formed crystals, while negative thoughts produce asymmetrical, non-formed crystals. In one experiment of Emoto and Radin's, there were 1,900 participants in Austria and Germany who focused their attention for three days on water samples that were in an electromagnetically shielded room in California, USA.

Water samples were near control water vessels, but these were not known to participants in the experiment. In addition, there were samples outside the sheltered room. Ice crystals were formed out of water, and the crystals were photographed. The ice crystal photos were evaluated by a group of 2,500 independent outsiders, according to which intentionally thought water samples produced more beautiful crystals than control crystals. The experiment repeated the results of previous pilot studies.

The rice experiment is a variation of Masaru Emoto's water experiments. It can also be performed in a home environment. In Emoto's rice experiment, boiled rice is put into three jars. On one jar, the word "Love" is written, on the second one "Hate," and the third jar is simply put aside without a label. It is completely ignored. In the experiment, as the name implies, love and positive feelings are directed toward the "Love" jar, and respectively, hate, anger and everything negative toward the "Hate" jar. As the experiment continues, the rice in the "Hate" jar will rot quickly, but the rice in "Love" jar will remain good for a long time. The third jar of rice, which is not taken into account in the experiment at all, rots even faster than the rice in the "Hate" jar. According to the experiment, the worst thing is to ignore something completely, as if it doesn't exist at all.

Both Masaru Emoto's ice crystal and rice experiments have been criticized for unscientific arrangements and for the fact that all information related to, for example, the freezing of ice crystals has not been shared to make the experiments repeatable. However, the fact that thousands of people who have done the rice experiment and are constantly reporting similar findings, tells us something. In my book, *From Quantum Physics to Energy Healing,* I describe doing a variation of the experiment myself, and I was really surprised that there was such a difference between the jars. I definitely recommend doing the test yourself.

Space is a creation?

Hiley and Pylkkänen point out in their study "Can mind affect matter via active information?" how the assumptions affect the conclusions drawn and thus, the results we get. In the case of repeatedly unsolvable problems, presuppositions should be considered, and thus the perspective from which the issue is considered. Hiley and Pylkkänen suggest that many problems in cognitive neuroscience, for example, including the hard problem of consciousness, are due to the view of reality based on classical physics. These problems could be clarified through the ideas of quantum physics. They don't suggest that quantum physics would necessarily solve everything, since quantum theory also has its limits. But an approach from the perspective of quantum physics can reframe the problems to help in the development of a new, more comprehensive theory. For example, if one thinks that the mind is both physical and mental and can function on a level completely different than what we've assumed, in which information is transmitted in the field and out of which one can influence the processes of the quantum world, perhaps the connection between the intangible and material worlds can be explained by Bohm's interpretation of quantum physics (the pilot wave theory).

Can mind – consciousness – affect the physical reality we live in? We don't have a theory that would explain the connection between mind and matter, but that doesn't mean it wouldn't be possible, as the documented examples presented in this chapter suggest.

It seems that distance doesn't matter, information travels regardless, non-locally, as the case of the Landau girls shows. It seems that quantum entangling occurs all the time, and not just for particles and atoms under laboratory conditions. It seems that two separate bodies or systems, separate in space, can be one and affect each other. While the space seems empty and the bodies seem to be separate, this is all just an illusion. Space would seem to be the creation of our perception, in the same way, for example, as the colors and shapes we perceive, the scents we smell, or the flavors we taste are.

We have the ability to influence one another and our physical reality, within certain limits. We are not separate, but instead part of a whole. We are connected to each other, like pieces of a puzzle. If we are pieces of a puzzle, do we still have the power to choose? Are we free to choose our place?

CHAPTER 8
DO WE HAVE FREE WILL?

Freedom is not a gift bestowed upon us by other men, but a right that belongs to us by the laws of God and nature.

—Benjamin Franklin

Did I have the freedom to choose to write this book? Could I have chosen otherwise? I have a feeling, at least, that I could have chosen some other topic, or even not to write a book at all. However, I remember how as a kid I wondered about reality. I remember thinking of questions like: *Do others hear that person talking in their mind, too? How can I be sure that when I go to sleep, I won't stay in that dream? How do I know what is real and what isn't?* Maybe I have been preparing myself from childhood to write this book? Maybe my destiny was sealed when I was born, and even though I have thought that I am making my own decisions, everything was already decided at the beginning of time?

Are we really free to make our choices, or is everything predetermined? This question is, in fact, essential for us, because we make decisions every day. The topic is also related to our views on life, religion, morality and well-being in many ways. Our experience is that we have free will, but only up to a certain point. I can decide to jump, but not all the way to the moon. By "free will" I mean exactly this kind of a freedom of choice, which has some limiting factors.

The problem of destiny and free will has been pondered already for centuries. Even in Ancient Greece, the philosopher Sophocles wrote about it in his tragedy, *Oedipus Rex*.

OEDIPUS

The father and mother of Oedipus were king and queen of Thebes. At Oedipus' birth, the oracle of Delphi made a prediction that when he grew up, he would kill his father and marry his mother. To avoid this, his father told his servant to kill the baby Oedipus. However, the servant did not obey, but left the boy in the woods where he was found and eventually raised as the foster son of the king of Corinth. Later, Oedipus heard from the oracle of Delphi about the prophecy and decided to leave Corinth because he thought the king and queen of Corinth were his parents. During his travels after leaving Corinth, he got into a quarrel and killed a man; it so happened that this man was the king of Thebes in disguise, his real father. Oedipus ended up in Thebes, where he solved the riddle of the Sphinx that had been holding the city hostage. As a reward, he was crowned king of Thebes and married the widowed queen, who was, unbeknownst to him, his mother. The prediction came true after all.

For us modern people, Oedipus is associated more with the Oedipus complex Sigmund Freud developed from the story, which attributes to sons a repressed desire to kill their fathers and marry their mothers. The real point of the story, however, is the question of whether we can act against our destiny, or whether destiny even exists.

So what is the relationship between destiny and free will? To what extent can we influence our destiny?

According to classical physics, everything is already decided

Our prevailing view of the world relies strongly on Newtonian classical physics and materialism, according to which our consciousness is the byproduct of brain activity. It could be described as an illusion created by our brain. According to classical physics, the universe is also characterized by determinism: Everything was already decided at the moment the universe was created. The whole of space-time arose at that moment, including all matter, particles, all interactions, all laws of nature. Each consequence is preceded by a cause and a future can be predicted according to the laws of classical physics. Thus, according to this view, we are helpless bystanders who only implement a ready-made model.

Proponents of determinism base their view on the fact that all phenomena are subject to the laws of nature, and the law of cause and effect prevails in nature. This means that all events follow from the preceding causes. Why this is the case one cannot explain. Also, since this reflects a law of nature, there can be no exceptions. Such causal determinism is very common in science. In addition to physics and chemistry, this kind of thinking has also spread to biology and neuroscience, such as the idea that your genetic makeup largely determines your destiny.

One argument often used to support this view comes from brain research. In brain imaging studies, it has been noticed that brain activity occurs 7 seconds before we become aware of making a choice. We, thus, have a conscious experience after there has been a change in the brain. Are we, then, only machines made up of neurons?

Quantum physics makes free will possible

According to Wolfgang Pauli, the mind-body division, an assumption established in the 17th century, never should have been made, since the result was a deterministic machine world. Studies of the atomic world forced us to take into consideration the fact of uncertainty in our accounts of physical phenomena. The impossibility of absolute accuracy suggests phenomena include a feature resembling free will. Pauli considered this to be natural, because the sources of our science and our experience are the same. Both strive to grasp reality. Rational science and a spiritual or mystical experience of immediate reality represent two complementary paths to understanding what is real.

Quantum physics, and especially the uncertainty principle of Heisenberg, demonstrates there is always uncertainty in measurement events and thus in our account of reality. The location of the particle cannot be described accurately; we can only present probabilities. The particle has alternatives, and both its past and future are uncertain. Modern physics is thus indeterministic. The determinism of classical physics must be replaced by the concept of statistical causality. We can describe how a large group behaves, but the exact fate of an individual event cannot be expressed with absolute certainty. Thus, statistical causality and free will are compatible. It can be said that at least at the particle level there is free will. Moreover, there is no reason to assume that the same would not be true when considering larger systems, because no limit in system size has yet been found beyond which quantum physics does not apply, as entanglement experiments show.

Moreover, according to Bell's theorem, one must reject determinism and give up a supposed objective reality that is measurable and observable. Thus, if quantum phenomena are reliable, determinism cannot be possible. Most physicists agree with this.

What do experiments tell us about free will?

We have an experience of free will and our brain takes part in forming this experience. The question of free will can be approached through experiments, where our senses and the subjective experience of the senses, thus the awareness of sense experiences, has been studied.

In studies, it has been shown that information about sensory stimuli travels to the brain at different rates. However, the mind feels as if information is being formed at the same time. According to classical physics, this could be explained by the fact that consciousness is only an illusion. Consciousness only creates the image that information arrives at the same time, but this is not the case in reality. If, on the other hand, it is assumed that this is a quantum phenomenon, the information can also go back in time. In quantum physics, we talk about the collapse of a wave function when a measurement observation is made, and since in quantum physics the direction of time is irrelevant, information can also move back in time.

When studying brain functioning many interesting phenomena have been observed that challenge physicalism. When for example you say something to another and he or she responds immediately, the activation in the responder's brain can be seen only after he or she has responded. It is as if the information really did travel from the answer to the past. The explanation given in neuroscience, based on physicalism, is that the responder answers unconsciously and later forms an illusion that the answer arrived consciously.

Affecting the past could be an important point when considering the question of free will.

Can information travel to the past?

Neuroscientist Benjamin Libet studied brain functioning and response studies at the University of California in 1979, in which he stimulated the patient's brain in specific areas and measured the electroencephalogram from the patient to see when the patient felt the stimulation. For example, he stimulated the brain area associated with the little finger from the brain and directly stimulated the finger, and measured the response time. One would think that the patient would feel the stimulation of the brain immediately and the stimulation of the actual little finger some time after this. However, the case was exactly the opposite. The EEG showed a peak describing activation 30 milliseconds after the finger was stimulated, and 500 milliseconds after the little finger area was stimulated in the brain. However, the operation was not yet conscious at 30 milliseconds. In order to produce the 30-millisecond peak generated by stimulation, stimulation and further brain activation had to take more than 500 milliseconds. The information thus travelled back in time.

A similar phenomenon has been observed in the studies of Bierman, Radin and Scholte, where the participants of the experiment were shown images at random speeds, and emotional response was studied. It was found out in the study, that the response to images happened 0.5–2 seconds *before* the images were shown. When studying quantum phenomena a similar phenomenon can be found: A conscious observer can freely decide how the particle is observed in the experiment, even afterwards, after the measurement has been done.

In a similar way – just as when you say something to another and he or she responds immediately – from the activation of the respondent's brain, of conscious doing, information travels to the past so that he or she can respond in real time and be consciously in control.

According to quantum physics we cannot know everything of the future; everything is not predetermined but instead occurs with a certain probability.

Our actions are not mechanically predetermined. Free will is, thus, possible according to quantum physics.

It is and it isn't

The biggest problem when considering the question of free will could be the inadequacies of our body and our perception. The experiments show that the information about an experience travels to our brain with different speed, depending on how it is measured.

What is most important to our lives is how we perceive reality to be. For example, I can write anything in this next sentence right now if I want to. Here I can put a squirrel jumping up and down, if I want to. I can freely plan alternative ways to proceed for this book. It has to be that way, since what point would there be in a life that has already been thought out in advance? If there was no free will, it would take the bottom out of our lives. For example, when someone commits a crime, we don't think it was his or her destiny. There is always freedom of choice, and we create what our lives turn out to be. We have free will, but within certain limits – just like a particle that obeys only statistical causality.

Philosopher and psychologist William James says: *"My first act of free will shall be to believe in free will."*

***

P.S. After I had written this chapter I carried the books back to the bookshelf. As I was placing the books on the shelf, one book dropped to the floor; it was called *Illusion of Freedom*. There was a yellow note on the cover saying it was *"Traveling book,"* meaning anyone can grab it when found and then pass it along. I had picked up the book from a coffee shop table years ago. I was left wondering: Had I come to the wrong conclusions in my chapter? Is freedom an illusion after all? Years ago, when I picked up the book, I was in no way familiar with this type of book, and there was nothing in that book that would have interested me then. However, I picked it up because there was something interesting in the title of the book. Maybe I was already heading towards this book at the time. Or was this book dropping from the shelf right now just a really good coincidence?

CHAPTER 9
COINCIDENCE OR SYNCHRONICITY?

> *Synchronicity is an ever present reality for those who have eyes to see.*
>
> —C.G. Jung

I am planning to write about coincidence and synchronicity, when YLE (Finnish National Broadcasting Company) writes on that same day (May 26, 2019) after Finland has won the Ice Hockey World Championships: "Unbelievable detail! 'The Groke' (from Moomin characters) Marko's winning goal was scored at exactly the same time as the winning goal that sealed the 2011 World Cup."

In both years, the winning goal was scored at exactly 42.35. And that's not all. On both occasions, the city was Bratislava, and even the gaming arena was the same. The head coach was Jukka Jalonen and the scorer was a player from the fourth line.

This is a good example of synchronicity. The probability that all these incidents would happen simultaneously is in practice impossible.

Synced in time

Carl Jung was the first to introduce the concept of *synchronicity*. By that he meant events that are "meaningful coincidences," that is, they occur with no causal relationship yet seem to be meaningfully related. The word *synchronicity* comes from the Greek words *syn*, together, and *chronos*, time, thus, "together in time." The word *coincidence* derives from Latin *com*, together, and *incidere*, to fall upon, and means "occurring together." Synchronicity, like coincidence, connects events that shouldn't have any connection at all but, following Jung, the connection is seen to be meaningful. For example, you desire an apple, and the next person you see asks if you would like an apple. Your wish comes true. The meaningful connection is formed by the event and your wish. There is, thus, a set of really improbably linked events that are synced in time, and besides that the events have some kind of a connection to the intention of their observer, either unconsciously or consciously. In addition, these events are meaningful to their observer.

Jung wrote in his article "*Synchronizität als ein Prinzip akausaler Zusammenhänge*" (Synchronicity – An Acausal Connecting Principle) in 1952, that his view is that events can have, besides a causal connection, one that is based on their meaningfulness. If the events have a meaningful connection, they don't necessarily need to have a causal connection. Jung introduced in his article the axiom of causality and suggested that the usual, everyday events typically have a connection that is both meaningful and causal, but in some special cases the causal connection can prematurely disappear. Needless to say, the idea of synchronicity has been rejected by the scientific community as impossible: The occurrence of events with a meaningful connection, between which there cannot be found any causal connection in the light of current knowledge, must be mere coincidence. However, we have certainly all encountered events the probability of occurrence of which is in practice impossible. Synchronicity can thus tell us something new about reality, and therefore needs to be studied more thoroughly.

GOLDEN SCARAB

Synchronicity was of interest to Jung, as in his research and work he often encountered events whose probability of simultaneous occurrence was nearly impossible. Jung was particularly intrigued by an incident concerning a young woman in treatment who told him about a dream of hers. In the dream, she was given a golden scarab, an amulet jewel designed like a beetle. As the woman was recounting her dream, Jung sat in his chair with his back to the window. Suddenly he heard a soft tapping sound behind him. Turning around, Jung saw an insect behind the window knocking on the windowpane. When he opened the window, a golden beetle (*Cetonia aurata*), the insect most resembling a scarab in those latitudes, flew into the room. For some reason, it wanted to fly to the dark room, and not be outside in sunshine. Jung had never experienced such a peculiar coincidence before, and he pondered it for a long time.

In particular, Jung noted how the young woman he was treating took the incident. The young woman's case had been really challenging, and there hadn't been much development in her state. Jung's view was that his patient was so firmly holding on to her own worldview, which was based very strongly on Cartesian philosophy, that she seemed to need a kind of "irrational shaking." Already the dream had been very vivid, but as the golden beetle flew into the room, the woman's attitude seemed to shift and move in a direction for the better. A change in attitude also means mental renewal, and Jung had found that this can often be figured in dreams in the form of various symbols. A scarab is actually a classic symbol of rebirth. In ancient Egypt, there was a god named Khebri who had a scarab as its head. Khebri signified the rising sun, creation, and rebirth. Jung also pondered how so many of us experience the same symbols in the same circumstances, as if the information were in our collective consciousness.

Jung had discussions about synchronicity with Einstein and Pauli, as he saw in synchronicity a connection to both relativity theory and quantum mechanics. With Pauli, Jung developed a model that would take into account both the mental and physical side of reality. Pauli held the mental side merging to the physical to be so important, that he considered physics to be incomplete until the connection to psychology has been established.

PAULI EFFECT

There were lots of synchronicities in Pauli's life, even so much that a specific "*Pauli effect*" was known. The following anecdote about Pauli is telling: It is well known that theoretical physicists and experimental work are not compatible: Experimental equipment has a tendency to break down. Pauli is often said to be such a "good" theoretical physicist that something broke as soon as he stepped into the lab. Once in Göttingen, in Professor J. Franck's laboratory, there was a sudden breakdown of equipment that initially seemed to have nothing to do with Pauli. From the early afternoon, for no apparent reason, the complex equipment for studying atomic phenomena suddenly collapsed. Franck wrote laughingly to Pauli's address in Zurich: "*As if Pauli had been there*!" In the return mail, he received a reply in an envelope bearing a Danish stamp. Pauli said he was meeting Bohr in Denmark, and at the time Franck's laboratory equipment broke down, his train had stopped for a few minutes at a Göttingen train station. So Pauli *had* been close to the equipment after all!

It should also be noted that the Pauli effect may also be a sign of psychokinesis, i.e. the PK phenomenon, in which the person's consciousness truly affects the equipment.

According to Jung, life is not a series of random events, but there is a deeper meaning. Synchronicity bears a resemblance to dreams, albeit occurring in everyday reality, and the purpose of synchronicity is to teach us. He considered the purpose of synchronicities to be to shift people's lives from self-centered, egocentric, thinking to a broader understanding, even spiritual awakening.

It seems that for many, noticing synchronicities is associated with better listening to oneself. Deepak Chopra, among others, also considers synchronicity important in human growth. Synchronicities expand perception, because they are surprising, and often gratifying. Sometimes they may even reinforce intuitive abilities. When you notice one, you notice another, and their number seems to increase. According to Chopra, synchronicity is a connection to one's own innermost being.

Explanation for synchronicity

Causality and synchronicity, i.e. acausality, are conceptually complementary. Synchronicity resembles the entanglement of quantum physics. There is a direct connection between two particles in entanglement, no matter how far apart they are. Synchronicity could be an indication that a similar flow of information is possible in the macro world as well. Perhaps synchronicity is an indication that information can also flow into the past, and thus be an indication of retrocausality? Maybe information flows in a field we are continuous with, and in some situations we become more aware of that information? Perhaps synchronicity could be explained by David Bohm's theory of implicit order or Rupert Sheldrake's morphic fields and extending the ideas of quantum theory to the macro level?

According to David Bohm's theory there exist three different ways of being: explicate order, which is the world we sense, accompanied by an implicate order, the world we experience in our minds. In addition, there is also consciousness, which enables and encompasses both worlds. The reality we perceive always takes on new visible, explicit, forms depending on the situation, i.e. the implicate order. There is a constant flow between the implicate and the explicate, the implicate also develops, gaining more and more diverse forms of emergence. Sometimes there can be a direct connection between implicate and explicate realities. Synchronicity could possibly be a bridge between these realities?

Rupert Sheldrake's morphic field hypothesis could also allow for synchronicity. The function of the human mind can also be described as the interaction of the morphic field with the psychochemical processes of the brain. Morphic fields extend widely around us and our surroundings, and they transmit information that we then perceive. The morphic field could also provide a possible explanation, besides synchronicity, for many other phenomena classified as paranormal. This could also explain how we sometimes know things that are considered to be in the collective consciousness, the "memory," even though we have never heard them before, such as Jung's golden scarab and its connection to the symbolic meaning of the scarab. All entities are connected to the same morphic field characteristic to them in which the information is transmitted.

Perhaps it would be possible to extend the ideas of quantum theory to the macro level? In fact, generalized quantum theory has already been developed. The hypothesis of Harald Walach *et al.* is based on the ideas of the quantum physical world including complementarity and entanglement. They consider certain physical and psychological variables and their correlations, utilizing both the ideas of quantum theory and systems theory. In the experimental arrangement, data are collected to the correlation matrix which is not time dependent, thus allowing events to occur in any order. The approach proposed by Walach's team is replicable and can be implemented by others.

The challenge in forming experimental arrangements is the difficulty of isolating the effects, that may interfere with the experiment, which in practice means isolating the causal signal from background noise.

Walach suggests that synchronicity means that we need to break free from causal thinking. It also makes it easier to understand phenomena that do not have a causal relationship, such as *psi* phenomena, that is, phenomena classified as parapsychological that are not within the reach of our normal five senses, such as telepathy, clairvoyance, and PK phenomena.

***

P.S. While I was writing this chapter, I suddenly realized when I was going to sleep, that my report to my remote healing customer hadn't left in the evening after the session, when I emailed it. I pressed the "Send" button and the message to my customer left at 1:27 a.m.

In the morning, she wrote back to me, "*Surprisingly, I woke up at 1:28 a.m., even though I had already slept well until morning after the treatments began. The time was pressed to my mind because it was exceptional. I had previously woken up in the morning at 4:44 a.m. or 3:30 a.m., for example, not this early, though. When I read your post the next day, I noticed that it had come at night at exactly the same time. It seemed thus to bring rather strong energy which awakened me. (I don't have a notifying sound that would inform me of emails.)*"

CHAPTER 10
IS TIME ONLY AN ILLUSION?

There is something essential about the 'now' which is outside the realm of science.

—Albert Einstein

"How long is forever?" asks Alice.

"Sometimes, just one second," replies the White Rabbit.

—Lewis Carroll, *Alice in Wonderland*

We live forwards, but we understand backwards.

—William James

I have to share a funny detail with you: I often have a commentator in my dreams who tells me how to interpret the dream. Once, I had a dream where the last words of my commentator were: "*...and the birdsong will be your sign for this.*" Exactly at that moment, I woke up to a loud birdsong right next to my open window. We were in the countryside in Germany and it was 4:05 a.m. The bird sang a dozen times "*Tweet-tweet-tweet, tweet-tweet-tweet....*" I closed the window and after a while the bird flew away. The rest of the night was peaceful and I slept well.

Before I fell asleep again, I was drowsily wondering: *What was the connection between my dream and the bird singing? Was I having a premonition in my dream that a bird will sing soon? Is it easier to receive information from the future in a dream, when we may be connected to a field of all information? Could it be so that the bird had somehow received the same information as I did and therefore it flew to sing a song by my window? Or is there no time at all in dreams and everything is already reachable right now? Maybe time disappears in dreams and it's just an experience we have while awake? I only wish I knew what the bird song was a sign of....*

What is time?

Nowadays, the general scientific belief is that our universe came into being with the "Big Bang," currently estimated to have occurred about 13.77 billion years ago. It is thought that the Big Bang also gave rise to time, as well as matter and the laws of nature, which the universe abides by.

In classical, Newtonian physics, time is thought of as separate from the material world, homogeneous, steadily advancing in one direction, and absolute. The direction of time is justified in physics using the second law of thermodynamics: The process of an isolated system proceeds toward its highest probability, that is, in the direction in which entropy, or disorder, increases and free energy decreases. Both time and space are infinite. Besides these, there exists a relative time, which measures duration, and which, unlike absolute time, is observable and used instead of real time. In classical physics, time is thought to be independent of the observer or the speed of the observer and is also measurable. This is how we usually perceive time in everyday life. We all have the same time. If I am late for a meeting, for example, I cannot justify that by appealing to my own personal time.

Time and space were understood as separate from each other until, in the theory of relativity, they were combined in the concept of space-time (special theory of relativity 1905, general 1915). According to the theory of relativity, both space and time depend on the observer's state of motion. There is no absolute time; it is impossible to determine simultaneity. In the theory of relativity, it is assumed that the flow of information has a maximum speed: Nothing can move faster than the speed of light. Simultaneity in different places thus always depends on the observer. The general theory of relativity also took into account the curving effect of mass on time-space. According to the theory of relativity, time is actually the result of the effect of gravity; it is said that gravity locally curves space-time. According to the theory of relativity, for objects moving close to the speed of light, time passes more slowly. Thus, if you time travel near the speed of light, the time passes more slowly for you than for your friends on the ground.

Time is considered in the theory of relativity to be one dimension in four-dimensional space-time, so-called Minkowski space. All events in the universe can, thus, be presented as one large map, where one point signifies one event, including the location coordinate and time of the event. Relativity enables, at least in theory, time traveling through "wormholes." It has even been suggested that particles, such as tachyons, would travel faster than light.

However, there is a contradiction in the time concept between the theory of relativity and quantum physics. Time is a problematic concept in physics. In quantum physics time is universal and absolute, and it doesn't have a direction. From the equations of quantum physics you cannot find a reason for why time would travel forward. In fact, you cannot find the direction in most of the other equations of physics either, not in the motion equations of Newton, in Maxwell's electrodynamics or in the theory of relativity. In quantum physics time is not a dimension. Time is not so essential a concept in quantum physics as it is, however, in classical physics. For example, there is no quantized time, as many other things in reality are quantized. Within the interpretations of quantum physics, time has been addressed in, among others, the Copenhagen interpretation and the many worlds interpretation.

In both quantum physics and the theory of relativity, the observer plays a key role. Absolute time and space cannot be reached, when it all depends on the observer. In modern physics, there is a very different subjective approach to reality than in classical physics. Reality has to be observed in a way very different from usual, taking into account the role of the observer, which also applies to time. Time is an experience. However, experiential time and the time of processes are different things. Processes always have a velocity at which they move forward.

There is no time at all?

If time is examined from a phenomenological, experiential perspective, it is a concept related to experience in the same way as colors, smells, tastes, sounds, shapes and space are. Usually, time refers to the order in which events occur.

The feeling of the passage of time is subjective. If you're having fun, two minutes fly by; if not, time goes slowly. We can measure the passage of time, and it creates the feeling that there is an absolute time that passes the same way for everyone.

French philosopher Henri Bergson's books, including *Creative Evolution* and *Time and Free Will* were very popular in the beginning on 20th century. Bergson proposed instead of objective time, the concept of personal, subjective time, which is best achieved through intuition. Maybe there is a personal time, after all, and I can invoke it the next time I'm late for an appointment? Bergson describes how "time" is a measure of change described by "duration." What separates the present from the past is that everything is new to us, but in a moment, it is already a memory and familiar to us.

If I meditate and I am able to receive information from the future and it is familiar to me, am I thus approaching a state where all information just is, and there is no time? Can we let go of time? Maybe eternal life means simply the disappearance of time? For example, in meditation or in a dream, it is possible to experience timelessness. In a dream, time seems to go by a different clock than everyday reality. You have probably experienced how, after just a moment of sleep, you wake up, and you have had several dreams, each depicting long periods of time. Just as in sleep, the clock of our experience would run faster than in everyday life, even though all the information already exists in the present. Maybe the frequency of receiving is different when we are sleeping compared to when we are awake?

In his book, *The End of Time*, Julian Barbour suggests that time, as we perceive it, doesn't exist. According to him, time is an illusion and many problems in physics are due to the fact that we assume time exists. Barbour argues we don't have any proof that the past exists besides our memory of it, nor any that the future does, except our belief in it. Change only creates an illusion of time, where every single moment is its own complete whole.

Maybe our life is like a movie? A movie consists of thousands of single images. Each image is static and exists, before the movie is watched. When the images are connected together, an impression is formed in the mind that makes it appear as if one image is changing into the next. We perceive continuity when the frames change, when our attention moves from one image to another. We thus experience static, timeless parallel realities, which exist simultaneously independent of each other. When we experience states one after the other, an impression of time is created. What we now call "movies" were called "living pictures" and "motion pictures" in the 19th and early 20th centuries, phrases that describe the phenomenon of still images seeming to move or come alive when displayed in rapid succession. If a viewer's attention isn't constantly on a movie, they experience isolated images appearing suddenly in front of them and see only parts of the movie. We only see some parts, but these form what we experience. Likewise, we thus create our "film," our own life. Time passes from one image we experience to another. Thoughts similar to Barbour's can be found in many religious and philosophical traditions. In Vedanta, for example, the cosmos is said to be created at the same time as the observer, and that there is no specific event of creation. Creation is continuous.

According to Barbour, the movie hypothesis would make it possible also to connect quantum physics to general relativity, in a theory of everything, the creation of which is often dreamt of. The hypothesis would also remove the need to assume there was a "Big Bang," the reason for which cannot be explained currently. We are so attached to deterministic thinking that it is difficult for us to imagine there not being an original state out of which everything is created. Why would there be this kind of a state that would exist before all other states? This is a classic chicken-or-egg problem.

Barbour is not alone in his thinking. Already in 1908, J.M.E. Taggart, in his book *The Unreality of Time*, proposed that time cannot be real, based on the fact that our definitions of time are either conflicting or inadequate. He shows this in his book and concludes temporality is not a feature of reality.

In the 1960s, physicists John Wheeler and Bryce DeWitt formed an equation that connects general relativity with quantum physics to quantum gravitation theory. What makes the equation special is that the term *time* is canceled and disappears completely in the equation. However, solutions have also been suggested to make it possible to fit time into the equation. The Wheeler-DeWitt equation explains how the boundaries between quantum physics and classical physics disappear due to gravity. Many consider it even more significant than the fundamental equation of quantum theory, the Schrödinger wave equation, which is the equation of the motion of particles in quantum physics.

In 2013, Ekaterina Moreva and her group at the Instituto Nazionale di Ricerca Metrologica in Turin, Italy, conducted an experiment that helped advance understanding of the Wheeler and DeWitt equation. In fact, already in the 1980s, Don Page and William Wootters proposed the entanglement of particles could be used to measure time. Moreva and her group built an experimental setup where a "mini universe" was created out of entangled photons and an observer-clock system, which was used to measure the change in polarization of particles in two different ways. The change in polarization between the particles in the arrangement was a measure of time. Different measurement methods showed the difference when the entangled particles changed their polarization. The result of the experiment has been interpreted as proving that time is an emergent phenomenon for observers inside the system, but it doesn't exist outside. In fact, this is also what the Wheeler and DeWitt equation predicts. An observer outside the universe would see only a static, unchanging universe. Based on the Moreva group experiment, should we also consider whether gravity is an emergent phenomenon that exists only for observers within the system, that is, in the universe?

Physicists Dmitry Podolsky and Robert Lanza have done interesting gravitation measurements using the Wheeler and DeWitt equation, and they have stated that it does not explain where the direction of time arises. Time would seem to be a property that depends on the observer's ability to "remember the past" – more technically, to record information about the events he or she is experiencing. The observer would thus appear to be creating the time he or she observes in the act of recording, that is, remembering.

Perhaps time is a side effect of how attention constantly shifts between billions of parallel realities? In films, the illusion of movement is created when the light beam of a film projector illuminates the images one after the other. The parallel realities are like images of film, static states, and consciousness is the film projector's light beam that creates the illusion of change and time as well as space. Images, or parallel realities, all exist and are equally real, and if you want to bring about change, a different reality, you have to change your perspective.

About the direction of time

Imagine time is a straight line. You can walk along the line in either direction. However, you cannot skip the points on the line, but you must pass through each point in either direction. You will have a memory of every point you have visited. Our experience is that we move forward at the same speed all the time. Time seems to move forward, for we remember the past, but not the future, at least in general. Our experience of time is that time goes on. Our experience of time is also constantly changing, as every present moment soon becomes a past moment, and the future the present.

The direction of time cannot be found in the equations of physics, and both physicists and philosophers have tried to find an explanation for it. In fact, one ought to talk about the direction of processes, since time isn't actually passing, but the physical processes are.

According to physicist Carlo Rovelli, there is no past or future. Time is relative, so it is irrelevant to know what is the absolute, the so-called correct time. There is no need to ask that. Time is not a separate feature of reality that just bounces past us unnoticed. Rovelli explains that time is *"a complex geometry woven together with space."* Moreover, time does not really exist, but is the result of our limited ability to perceive. We experience time as a parallel due to the second law of thermodynamics, according to which the universe progresses toward an ever-increasing disorder, entropy (Greek *en,* diverging, divisive and *tropos,* tendency). The ice cube, which is dropped into the tea cup, melts and cools the tea water, forming a cooled mixture of tea and water, and they never again separate into ice and tea at different temperatures. For that to happen, it would take energy. As entropy grows, there are more and more options, possibilities.

Naturally, considering entropy, one would assume that in the beginning there was an order in which entropy increases. Some physicists have sought to explain this feature with the parallel universe model, where time could also pass in the past, or in any direction.

However, the growth of entropy alone does not explain the direction of time. In stochastic, i.e. statistical, systems entropy does increase, but in nature this is not always the case. In fact, entropy sometimes even seems to decrease. For example, why are we not just elementary particles, but matter instead? Could consciousness be an explanatory factor for the difference between living and inanimate systems?

Entropy and time are related to our experience, our perception of reality. Causality, or cause-and-effect, is also closely linked to these.

For the sake of fairness, or actually complementarity, entropy also has an opposite, as in physics there usually is, namely syntropy (Greek *syn*, converging and *tropos*, tendency). There is also information that travels in the same direction with syntropy. In 2007, Antonella Vannini formulated the following hypothesis: "*If life is sustained by syntropy, the parameters of autonomic nervous systems that support vital functions, should react in advance to stimuli (retrocausal activation).*" In several experiments before the hypothesis was proposed, changes were noticed in conductance measurements of skin and in heartbeat. Radin, Spottiswoode and May conducted experiments where the reactions of individuals participating in the tests were studied before they were shown different kinds of images. First, the test subjects watched an empty screen for five seconds and then they were shown at random either a peaceful or an emotional image for three seconds. In the experiments, a significant increase in the conductance of skin was noticed 2–3 seconds before showing emotional images. In several other similar experiments changes have been observed in the parameters of the autonomic nervous system. Maybe syntropy is a feature related to living systems where consciousness has a role? And what could retrocausality tell us about time and reality?

Retrocausality

Maybe it is time for us to change our conception of time. Maybe time is only a product of our limited understanding, and we ought to examine its features more carefully. One interesting phenomenon linked to time is retrocausality.

In retrocausality an effect may precede a cause. An event from the future can affect this moment or the past, as if information could travel in a direction opposite to our experience of time. This means, for example, that when the performer of the experiment chooses how to observe particles, the choice affects what properties they reveal about themselves. This is also not in conflict with the laws of thermodynamics.

The possibility of retrocausality arose especially with modern physics, as the equations of quantum theory are symmetric regardless of the direction of time. There is no obstacle for time to pass in either direction. Thus, such time symmetry also supports retrocausality. In fact, there are no obstacles in other theories of physics for information to travel from the future to the present or past. Both Newton's laws of motion and the theory of relativity work in the same way, whether we look at a phenomenon that moves in the same or opposite direction as time.

J.B. PRIESTLEY AND PREMONITIONS

British author and journalist J.B. Priestley had been curious all his life about the mystery of time, dreams and premonitions. He also thought that the Western Newtonian way of conceptualizing time had been the biggest mistake we had ever made. He thought dreams and premonitions were one example of our erroneous idea of time. Priestley asked people to send their experiences to him. As a journalist, Priestley was very popular and he received hundreds of letters describing premonition dreams and everyday events that, according to the writers, had predicted future events. The premonition might take the form of a surprising change in behavior: For example, a person suddenly begins to behave strangely in relation to the current situation, such as bursting into tears suddenly when they see a certain building with which he should have no known connection; later, it would be discovered that the reaction was related to future events.

In his book, *Man and Time* (1964), Priestley describes his experiences and concludes the future affects the present moment. He observed, for example, that the body seems to react to future events before the mind, and often so that the conscious mind of the person understands this only afterwards. This had not been observed before. Priestley's observations received publicity, but were not seriously considered before the year 2010 when Professor Daryl Bem from Cornell University studied a similar phenomenon and how the body reacts in nine experiments with thousands of participants. Eight of these experiments had statistically significant results, which validated the observations Priestley had already made, that the human body really reacts to future events in advance.

There are other collections and studies similar to those of Priestley and Bem. The laboratory research results from the field of parapsychology, accumulated over more than 100 years, are a proof that we sometimes receive information regardless of time and distance. These results cannot be explained by conventional means. The studies carried out by Robert Jahn and Brenda Dunne in Princeton's PEAR laboratory, the studies by Russell Targ at the Stanford Research Institute, and the data gathered by J.B. and Louise Rhine at the Rhine Research Center suggest that information and time do not go causally hand in hand.

RUSSELL TARG AND REMOTE VIEWING EXPERIMENTS

In Remote Viewing (RV), subjective impressions of different objects are sought using different techniques regardless of time and place. The viewer does not know anything about the objects in advance, nor do the other participants during the collection of information. The method was initially developed at the Stanford Research Institute in the 1970s for the US military to gather information during the Cold War about the opponent's submarines, the site of bases and other movements.

It is possible to receive information using RV from the distant locations, and even time doesn't matter; the events can be in the distant past or the future. The thinking differs so much from what we are used to that the results of RV research have not always been easy to understand and they have often had to be proven.

For example, when physicist Russell Targ, one of the developers of the method at the Stanford Research Institute, wanted to publish his group's results in one scientific research journal, the editor-in-chief of the paper didn't approve at first. Instead, he asked them to demonstrate what it was all about. If they could convince him, he would publish the results in the journal. The editor-in-chief owned a technology company, and he selected a few of his engineers to conduct the remote viewing test. For five days, the editor-in-chief hid at a randomly selected destination in a nearby town. Prior to this, the engineers did remote viewing after Targ taught them the RV technique; they had written down their observations based on looking in advance at where the editor-in-chief would be at the time. After conducting five tests, the editor-in-chief read all five recorded observations, and they perfectly matched his hiding places on different days. The probability of this was 0.008 according to their estimates. The editor-in-chief finally agreed to publish their research findings.

LOUISE RHINE AND PREMONITION DREAMS

In the 1950s, L.E. Rhine gathered data in the United States on premonition dreams and experiences, and she noted that 75% of premonition experiences were dreams. Sannwald studied the same in Western Europe in 1963 (60% premonition dreams), Orme in England in 1974 (74% premonition dreams), and similar figures have been presented by Steinkamp (2000) and Drewes (2002). Usually the premonition dreams are highly realistic, such as seeing someone in a dream get in an accident. In her research, Louise Rhine wondered why premonitions are so often dreams. Could it be that in normal day-to-day mental life, the conscious mind rules out all such unpleasant information and it is only in dreams when the defense mechanism doesn't work that access to this kind of information is possible? It is easier for us to treat dreams as messages of the unconscious mind than what we experience in everyday life. Louise Rhine also found that events in dreams are always perceived to occur simultaneously, even premonition dreams are never perceived to occur in the future, but are seen as if they were happening right now.

WHEELER'S DELAYED CHOICE THOUGHT EXPERIMENT

Physicist John Wheeler proposed a thought experiment that is a variation of the famous double slit experiment; in it, a particle travels through two slits so that out of the two slits the other one may be closed after the particle has passed the slits but before it hits the wall. The question, thus, follows: When does a particle get the information that one of the slits is closed? How fast does the information flow?

Courtney Brown's group has carried out some remote viewing experiments at the Farsight Institute, where this kind of influencing of the past has been studied in practice. In their remote viewing experiments the object chosen and viewed remotely was in the past. Their job was thus to find out what the event was that they were remote viewing. The remote viewers did the experiment and the results were strictly encrypted. The data were made publicly available in encrypted form before the subject itself was randomly selected a couple of weeks *after* the remote viewing was done. The site was selected by an external person (a professor who did not otherwise have access to the data in any way), after which the password to open the data was made available. If the results were not strictly encrypted and the target was in the future, the results were not so good. It even seemed that the remote viewers saw the experimenter's perceptions of what might be happening and not the event itself. Maybe they had nothing else to grab except the thoughts of the organizer of the experiment?

It has often been thought that retrocausality cannot be distinguished from regular causality based on Heisenberg's uncertainty principle, and because of this the true significance of the phenomenon hasn't really been considered.

Eric Wargo discusses the idea of retrocausality in his book *Time Loops: Precognition, Retrocausation, and the Unconscious*, and he comes to some interesting conclusions. Wargo describes our world in an unfamiliar way by presenting the time and cause-effect relationship as a cycle, a "time loop." He discusses several cases where people have "remembered" their future. Our world would seem to be full of self-fulfilling predictions, and we usually don't even notice these. One example of this is how the researcher influences the passage of light in the past by measuring the motion of photons now, as is done in the double-slit experiment. Perhaps the observation in the future at the moment when the particles are detected does affect the moment when they are measured? In the double-slit experiment, it can even be decided much later after the experiment how the particles are detected and the results are consistent with it. Time does not matter, nor does distance.

Wargo also thinks our dreams are one way for us to receive information from the future. Dreams tell us about our reactions and feelings. There is a lot of data suggesting dreams have anticipated such events as the sinking of the Titanic and 9/11 and have even influenced people's decisions. For example, on the four planes that crashed on 9/11, there were on average fewer passengers than usual on the corresponding Tuesday mornings, with a load factor of only 33%. According to Wargo, dreams are not the journey of the mind to the future, but they anticipate our future feelings; that is, what we feel when we come to hear about events, like when we read the news or hear about it from someone. Perhaps synchronicities also indicate such anticipation?

According to Ulisse Di Corpo, in the present moment, there is both past and future, causality and retrocausality. The past has already been observed, and it is causal, that is, it has a particle nature, while retrocausality means unlimited possibilities, that is, it has a wave nature (probability wave). Thus, according to this interpretation, for example, both causality (particle nature) and retrocausality (wave nature) can be observed in a double-slit experiment. Reality, thus, has to be a constant interaction of past and future information on a physical level, and we also experience it through our own feelings and thoughts. We anticipate things and direct our attention to the future even though the future is not determined. In one study, US train accident statistics were examined and it was discovered that the trains involved in accidents had significantly fewer passengers than usual. Similar results have also been found in plane-crash investigations. Maybe we often make choices based on anticipation without noticing or knowing why?

Julia Mossbridge and Theresa Cheung have written a book called *The Premonition Code,* where they explain how anticipating the future can be learned. Retrocausality can, for example, allow artists and writers to see their finished work and remember their future when creating their work. Of course, I decided to try this while writing this book.

Time is not we think it is, or what it seems to be in everyday life. Jeffrey Mishlove represents an interesting viewpoint on retrocausality in his "New Thinking Allowed" YouTube series: Mishlove discusses the book *The Reflexive Universe – Evolution of Consciousness* by Arthur M. Young. He writes about the reflexivity of the universe. Reflexivity refers to circular relationships between cause and effect – a kind of reflection, contemplation and development based on it. Mishlove brings up the concept of virgin birth, which is also mentioned in the Bible. Perhaps retrocausality suggests that possibly the universe could have given birth to itself?

Retrocausality has also been suggested as a solution to the theory of everything, that is how to fit quantum physics to relativistic physics. The connection between entanglement and retrocausality has also been considered. Maybe the connection of particles in entanglement is formed based on retrocausality? The question of free will also comes to mind when considering retrocausality. If one thinks that different points in time and, for example, the future have an effect on the present moment, is it really possible to choose freely between different options in this moment? Maybe everything is really partially decided, and the options out of which we choose are limited? However, we have the experience of free will. In any case, all the data suggest that in certain situations it is possible for us to get information that seems to come from another time and another place.

Time is a byproduct

The following sentence describes well the shift in thinking that is needed:

> *In reality, time and space exist in you. You do not exist in them.*
>
> —Sri Nisargadatta Maharaj

The sources I have presented above all seem to point in the same direction. It would seem that time is subjective and we have an experience of time, but it doesn't really exist. Reality is independent of both place and time, that is, non-local and also timeless.

In fact, the idea that there is no time and space is not at all unusual, and not even new. The mathematician Gottfried Leibniz (1646–1716) developed his own theory to explain reality, where time and space do not exist. Leibniz thought that the time and space we experience in everyday life are projections of a more real reality where there is no time and space.

Time would seem to be a byproduct that arises when we locally observe timeless events we experience momentarily. Barbour suggests that timeless events are linked to each other due to their similarity through a certain set of rules, and they make consecutive experiences look causal. These also seem to have a common physical basis, the laws of physics. We can also get information beforehand from the future, because information can also travel to the past.

If the theory of relativity and quantum mechanics could be united under the same theory, we could have a model that would also explain time. What would thus quantized space-time mean?

CHAPTER 11
QUANTIZED SPACE-TIME

The book of nature is written in the language of mathematics.

—Galileo Galilei

While I have been writing this book, interesting things have started to happen – as if I'm being guided to read exactly the right articles and books, to discuss ideas with certain people, or just notice certain things. And if I don't notice them right away, they will come back to me even more clearly. As I start to write this chapter about the theory of everything, on the same morning I receive an email saying the Natural Philosophy Society of Finland is organizing an international seminar in Helsinki and the topic is "Unification in Physics and Philosophy." This is so timely: I just need a view into the current state of this topic of combining theories and the theory of everything. After all, one could assume that if the theories can be combined into one whole, it would at the same time offer answers about the nature of reality. A lecture on theoretical physics comes to my mind: When I was studying physics at the university, the lecturer mentioned how happy we should be to live during this time when we may finally begin to get answers to our questions about the nature of reality. I immediately registered for the seminar.

What is the theory of everything?

The "theory of everything" (TOE) is an all-encompassing theoretical framework that unites all current theories of physics, explaining all known interactions and forces. Physics is actually full of mysticism, or magic, when you think more closely – for instance, think of non-local forces, which act from a distance.

There are four different forces in currently recognized science: one is electromagnetic force, that rules over matter. It occurs between electrically charged particles. The second force, strong interaction, holds atomic nuclei together; the third, weak interaction, acts between subatomic particles and is thus responsible for the radioactive decay of atoms. The fourth force is gravitation, which is the weakest of the four, but because it acts on large masses, its overall impact is large. All these forces have their own "magic particle," an elementary particle that mediates the interaction. Photon is the mediator of electromagnetic force, gluon the mediator of strong interaction, intermediate boson of weak interaction and graviton of gravitation. All these forces behave in the same way as the light we know well, which is electromagnetic radiation: Sometimes they behave like particles, sometimes like waves. The all-encompassing theory that would combine all these forces would explain, at least in principle, all known natural phenomena, and thus one could assume that it would also explain what reality is.

The theory of everything has been the dream of physicists since the early 20th century. Originally, the idea of unification was based on the understanding that magnetic and electrical phenomena have a connection. Electricity affects magnets and magnets create an electric current. Maxwell's equations, named after their developer James Clerk Maxwell, describe this connection and form the basis of electromagnetism. Gradually during the 20th century, one by one, interactions have been unified under different theories (Figure 10).

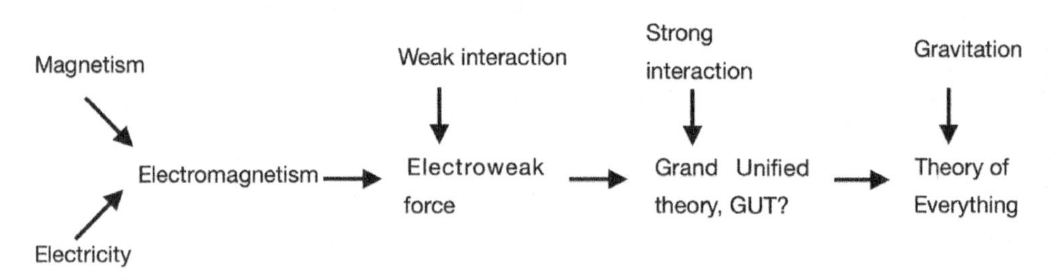

FIGURE 10. UNIFYING THE INTERACTIONS.

The theory of the electroweak force connecting electromagnetism and weak interaction was developed in 1976, and the combination of these was experimentally proved later in the 1970s and 1980s. The finding of the electroweak force further supported the idea that there was a time in the universe when all forces were one, perhaps at the time of the Big Bang. The Grand Unified Theory (GUT) combines the electroweak force and strong interaction. There are several models for a potential GUT. Experimentally, however, electroweak force and strong interaction have not been combined. The reason for this is that the further to the right you go in the picture, the higher the energies are to detect the forces. Combining gravity with the GUT would mean the theory of everything. Often the Grand Unified Theory and the theory of everything are discussed together. In practice, one might think that the GUT also enables the development of the theory of everything.

In the general theory of relativity, electromagnetic force and gravity are combined. Until his death, Einstein sought to develop a theory of everything, but he wasn't successful. Perhaps the reason was that he could not accept quantum mechanics and thus build his theory on the basis of it. In 1948, Feynman, Schwinger, and Tomonaga developed the quantum electrodynamic theory that also took relativity into account. They received the Nobel Prize in Physics in 1965. The theory describes the behavior of charged particles in an electromagnetic field and is considered a theory of everything for particles; it is often called the standard model. However, the true theory of everything in physics would consider the fields as well. There are some physicists who consider the development of a theory of everything an impossible idea.

Is string theory the solution?

Especially toward the end of 20th century, string theory, sometimes called M theory, was proposed as a solution. String theory, which I will describe below, may be the most well-known hypothesis for a theory of everything. However, there are physicists, such as Carlo Rovelli, who consider the pursuit of a unified theory too ambitious. He suggests that if we were able to combine quantum mechanics and gravity, it would lead our understanding toward the theory of everything.

General relativity describes how gravitation curves space-time. Quantum mechanics, instead, describes particle-level phenomena. Both work well in describing the phenomena observed in the universe, one at the macro and one at the micro level. The problem is to combine these, as they would seem to be in conflict. The theory of relativity does not take into account the quantum nature of reality, nor quantum mechanics the time-space curving effect of gravity. This is called the problem of quantum gravity, to which the equation of Wheeler and DeWitt, which I mentioned earlier, also seeks to find answers. However, the interpretation of the equation has been challenging due in part to the time variable disappearing from the equations. However, Smolin and Jacobson stated in the 1980s that they would get a solution to the equation of Wheeler and DeWitt if they assumed there were loop-like structures in space. This was the beginning of the development of loop quantum gravity theory. The theory thus takes into account the quantum nature of space-time. It is not really a theory of everything, but it would solve many challenges. It may be that both string theory and loop quantum theory ultimately lead to the same understanding of reality.

ABOUT STRING THEORY AND HIGHER DIMENSIONS

Although string theory is no longer considered an established solution for the theory of everything, it has led to discoveries of some interesting features of reality. In string theory, the universe is thought to consist of extremely small strings that vibrate in several dimensions. Naturally, such strings have not been observed, as the strings are hypothesized to be in the size range of Planck length (1.6×10^{-35}m). Planck length is the shortest length that can be used in measurements involving the velocity of light, general relativity and the uncertainty principle of Heisenberg. String theory is, thus, based on the assumption of the existence of higher dimensions. While we may speak of higher dimensions in everyday life, these dimensions do not (necessarily) mean the same as the spatial dimensions of string theory.

The physical world we experience is three-dimensional. We usually describe it with three spatial coordinates, plus time, which is often considered as the fourth dimension. Time was Einstein's addition to the space dimensions. Thus, Minkowski's space-time has (x, y, z, ct) coordinates, where x, y and z indicate the spatial location, c is the speed of light, and t is time. Time is thus one existing dimension, similar to space coordinates.

Using these four coordinates it is possible to describe in space and time any event in the universe. For example, as I am writing this, the world celebrated the 50th anniversary of the first lunar walk, and that event can be placed in a space-time coordinate system covering the entire universe, as well as all other events with their locations and times.

So, are there higher dimensions than these we know? A fifth dimension or even higher dimensions? If time is counted as the fourth dimension, then the next dimension would be the fifth dimension, or if only the space dimensions are considered, it would then be the fourth space dimension.

Originally, the idea of using higher dimensions came from the Finnish physicist Gunnar Nordström, who suggested the fifth dimension could solve the problem of combining gravity and electromagnetic force. Gravity would be the curvature of four-dimensional space and electromagnetism would be the curvature of the fifth dimension. Kaluza and Klein also came to same conclusions. Their theory suggested that light is vibration of the fifth dimension. The fifth dimension also made it possible to combine gravity and light. These conclusions were also important later in string theory.

The challenge in observing higher dimensions is that we cannot see higher than the current three, or including time, four dimensions. You can see for yourself this way: Take a paper and put it on the table in front of you. Draw a worm, whatever kind you like. The worm you drew is two-dimensional. It exists on paper, in the 2D world. The worm can move in two dimensions, it can move anywhere on the paper. However, it doesn't have any idea of the third, higher dimension. It doesn't know that someone is watching it, since that happens in a dimension higher than where it lives; for the worm, you are in the so-called hyper dimension. It can observe lower-level dimensions, that is, the 1D world, which is a line, or the 0D, which is a point. It can only experience a higher dimension, or 3D, when someone or something brings it into that dimension, that is, lifts it out of that 2D plane of the paper, and it is able to view it from the outside in 3D. However, as a two-dimensional worm, it may not even be able to perceive three-dimensionality, and the experience is incomprehensible for it.

Mathematically one can thus calculate equations of multidimensional spaces, but there is no answer to what these mean and whether they could exist. There may possibly be higher space dimensions, but we cannot comprehend them, at least with our current five senses in the 3D world.

However, it would seem that if there existed higher dimensions, many of the problems in physics would disappear. According to physicist Michio Kaku, there is not enough room in the 3D world to make the laws of physics work together. We see only loose parts, such as quantum physics, which explains particle-level phenomena, and the theory of relativity, which works close to the speed of light, but to combine the theories, assumptions need to be made that are difficult to justify. It is easier to see the whole if there are extra dimensions. In string theory the universe is thought to consist of strings that vibrate in several dimensions. The size range of the strings is of the size of the smallest measurable length, i.e. Planck length. In practice, this means the smallest possible size for a particle, smaller than that collapsed into a black hole. According to some string theory calculations, the universe could have 10 or 11 dimensions. Even more than 11 dimensions have been calculated, but with 10–11 dimensions the whole would still be quite stable and would not disintegrate. The higher dimensions must be very small, smaller than atoms, for otherwise the atoms would disappear into another dimension, and with them, therefore, all matter and our universe.

It is possible that the universe around us is hyperdimensional, but we can't see these dimensions. One suggestion is that the dimensions are curved and too small for us to see. It has also been suggested that gravity might be the link between different dimensions. Maybe black holes are a sign that matter flows from our universe to other dimensions?

String theory could also explain why the universe is expanding. According to the theory, the Big Bang would have been preceded by a 10- or 11-dimensional universe that was not stable enough and split in two into the current four-dimensional and additionally a 6- or 7-dimensional universe. As a result of disintegration, our universe began to expand and another universe shrank even further. The reason for the expansion would thus be the collapse of the space-time of the original 10- or 11-dimensional universe.

The problem of string theory is that it is in practice impossible to test. Physicists have concluded that by measuring gravitational waves, possible evidence of the existence of extra dimensions could be obtained. Gravitational waves are disturbances in the curvature of space-time, and are due to the motion of masses curving space. However, testing the actual theory of everything would require energy on the order of 10^{19} GeV. This is called Planck energy. When the energy of a particle is increased close to the energy of Planck, its gravitational interaction approaches other basic interactions at the same time. To test this, a particle accelerator larger than the solar system would be needed.

The discovery of the Higgs boson in 2013 was not yet proof of the functionality of string theory. The discovery of the Higgs boson is said to confirm that the theory of everything for particles, the standard model, is valid. It was expected in the experiment that supersymmetric particles would also have been found to confirm the assumptions of string theory, but these were not found. However, the absence of observation does not yet prove anything.

LOOPS INSTEAD OF STRINGS?

In loop quantum gravity higher dimensions are not assumed. The approach to combining quantum mechanics and relativity theory is much simpler than in string theory. The theory uses existing theories in an effort to find an answer to what quantized space-time is like. Thus, it is not built on the basis of experimental data like many other theories but on the belief that quantum mechanics and relativity theory are correct. Einstein proposed in relativity theory that time and space are representations of gravitational (force) field, and they change based on the gravitational field. Quantum mechanics taught that all fields of interaction are quantum fields, and thus have both a particle- and a wave-like nature. This is also the case in space-time. The quantification of space-time sets boundaries on time and space. For instance, just as the pixel is the smallest component of a digital image, the smallest possible size of space is measured in Planck length. Smolin and Jacobson assumed that space is a gravitational field formed by such finite Planck-length-sized loops. Space is not continuous and shapeless, but has boundaries.

In the same way, time is not a separate stream passing by us, but a local phenomenon that depends on who perceives it when and where. Time is thus involved in interaction. When quantification is taken into account, time becomes irrelevant. Events are no longer arranged causally in succession over time, as the law of causality does not work at the quantum level. The disappearance of the time term in the Wheeler and DeWitt equation is therefore correct. In quantized space-time, events can be in any order. An example of this could well be synchronicity or retrocausality.

Quantized space-time, thus, means that if quantum mechanics is taken into account, both time and space change. There is no separate time and space, but instead both are representations of quantum fields. Time is actually a measure of change. It only tells how things organize themselves in relation to each other. Time that we use in our everyday life is accurate enough to describe change, but it doesn't work anymore on the micro level. This is also true for space, which is also a creation of quantum fields and observable only on a macroscopic level that is the level on which we live.

The supposition of loop quantum theory that there is no time and space is in fact compatible with the ideas of Leibniz from the late 17th century. Although Leibniz's theory was proposed over 300 years ago, it has amazing similarities with quantum mechanics. Soshichi Uchii from the University of Kyoto considers Leibniz's ideas as a way to combine quantum theory and general relativity. According to Leibniz, the time and space that we experience in everyday life are projections of a more real reality where there is no time and space. Time is just a sign of events that have been successfully experienced, a kind of "collapsed" or perceived reality. He also accepted the idea familiar from Vedanta of the continuous creation of a space associated with every moment, between which, however, the transition is not continuous. According to Leibniz, the cause-and-effect relationship we perceive in everyday life is only apparent. When we find that A causes B, this happens only seemingly and only the states that cause these events adapt to each other, creating this impression. The change in the event itself takes place independently, although it can be triggered by a change somewhere else.

At the level of everyday life, then, we see a reality that is only an approximation of the real reality, even though for us it is more real than anything else.

So far quantum gravitation is just a theory, but it could explain the connection between our microscopic and macroscopic worlds. The theory has not yet been experimentally proven to work, but time – if you can say that when there is no time – will tell what its destiny may be.

The theory of everything is a dream that would solve many open questions. Our view of the universe is largely based on assumptions, such as what we assume the structure of the universe to be.

Dark matter and dark energy?

According to NASA's current calculations the universe consists of 4.6% atoms, 24% dark matter and the rest, 71.4%, is dark energy. The visible matter we perceive accounts for less than 5% of the universe; the remaining 95% is invisible and unreachable. All this came into being, according to the prevailing understanding, in the Big Bang.

Dark matter and dark energy are needed to explain how the universe behaves. According to the calculations done there should be much more mass in the universe than what visible matter accounts for. Galaxies behave as if they consisted of something much heavier. Dark matter and dark energy are needed to explain this difference.

Dark matter is an enigma. It has been theorized for almost 90 years, but little is known about it. It has not been observed directly. Dark matter can only be detected through gravity and weak interaction; that is, information about its properties can only be obtained by studying how it affects visible matter. It is known to be matter with mass, but it does not absorb or emit light like the matter we see. A neutrino is an example of dark matter. In 1930, Wolfgang Pauli hypothesized that radioactive beta decay must generate a particle in order to maintain momentum in the decay. The particle had to be electrically neutral and share energy with the electron. Twenty years later, the neutrino hypothesis was confirmed by studying the operation of nuclear reactors. When they work, so many neutrinos are produced that they could also be detected with measuring devices. Neutrinos have no electrical charge, so they cannot be affected by magnetic or electric fields, and it was long thought that they had no mass. They permeate almost all matter, as they interact in practice only through weak interaction. Neutrinos are said to be *hot* dark matter as they move at very high speeds; in some experiments their speed was found to be even higher than the speed of light – which is in contradiction with the theory of relativity. However, the results of that 2011 experiment at CERN in Switzerland were soon withdrawn, citing the problems with the system used to measure time.

According to current knowledge dark matter speeds around the universe unevenly. In May 2019, strange holes were reported to exist in the Milky Way star stream. An as-yet-unknown phenomenon had burst into the giant holes in our galaxy's largest stellar stream called GD-1, 30 to 65 light-years wide in diameter. The holes looked as if some very dense object had swept through the stellar stream, throwing isolated stars around. Dark matter is considered a possible alternative explanation for the formation of holes. The finding would support the hypothesis that dark matter is unevenly present in the universe.

The future of the universe depends on the amount of mass in it. The universe is expanding and it appears to be doing so at an accelerating speed. That should not be the case, because the mass in the universe should slow expansion, just like when you throw a ball. Eventually, it drops to the ground under the influence of Earth's gravity. The prevailing notion in the first half of the 20th century was that the universe was eternal and also unchanging. Einstein thought so too. In solving the equations of the general theory of relativity, the surprising answer was that the universe seemed to be expanding. To correct his assumed error, Einstein developed a cosmological constant for his equation that allowed all solutions depending on the value of the constant: expansion, shrinkage, and staying stable. The value of the constant only had to be determined in order to know the future. Willem de Sitter further developed the theory, arguing that in space, objects really go farther apart from each other. The reason for this conclusion was the observed redshift phenomenon, including in the case of helium stars. In redshift, as the object and observer move away from each other, the wavelengths are perceived at higher wavelengths than the original, i.e., they move closer to the red wavelength, hence the name redshift.

The redshift phenomenon has been explained by the fact that the light from distant objects set off when space was smaller than it is today. During the journey, the wavelength of light has increased in proportion to the scale of space. Edwin Hubble observed that the farther apart the objects are, the greater the redshifts, which means that the objects move away from each other faster the farther apart they are. The increase in distances is not due to objects hurrying away from us at high speeds, but because the entirety of space is expanding.

De Sitter's idea was also to add invisible mass to the universe in addition to the visible matter, to ensure that the mass of space is homogeneous with cosmological distances. It is known how the universe behaves, and how much matter there should be to reproduce the behavior.

The idea of an expanding universe was unpleasant to many physicists and cosmologists. Einstein didn't like the idea either, and it was especially difficult for him to accept the thought that the universe might have a beginning. However, he gradually had to approve this as Hubble provided evidence that the universe is expanding.

In the 1990s, it was observed that the expansion of the universe was accelerating, from which it was concluded that there must be something else in the universe as well. This was called dark energy. It is not known what it is, but how it behaves is known. Dark energy is assumed energy that fills the entirety of space and pushes galaxies away from each other. Galaxies themselves cannot expand because gravity is a stronger force than the effect of dark energy. The proportion of dark energy determines the rate at which the universe expands. Einstein's theory predicts all of this. The current expectation, then, is that the universe will continue to expand at an accelerating rate unless there is some reason why it would stop accelerating.

We know that the material world is only a small part of the universe. Maybe we should consider space, that bigger part, instead of the smaller one? Maybe space, whatever it is, determines matter and therefore us?

Dark energy is a hypothesis, and its nature or the possible carrier particle is not known. Dark matter and energy are, however, the prevailing view of science about the universe. The assumption of dark matter and dark energy is accepted, but, for example, the fundamental role of consciousness or its connection to physical reality is not, even though each of us has experience of consciousness. Why this is so, I have no answer.

What if we are discussing the same issue, but with different terms? Maybe dark matter is consciousness, which is "materializing"? Or just another galaxy in a parallel universe? Maybe we move in death to another dimension when matter lets go, and spirit, soul is free? Do we then also have the freedom to choose?

These questions are thought to belong to the realm of metaphysics, philosophy or religion, but the theory of everything should give an answer to these as well.

There are also hypotheses that do not rely on dark matter or energy, as some scientists do not believe in their existence at all. The Big Bang theory has also been questioned, although at present the experimental data seem to suggest that everything started from one point, the singularity. In terms of the theory of relativity, singularity is the point where the curvature of space-time is infinite.

A.F. Ali (Benha University and the Zewail City of Science and Technology) and S. Das (University of Lethbridge) suggest in a peer-reviewed Physics Letter B paper a model according to which the universe has always existed. Their work was based on the quantum trajectory model, which was suggested by physicist David Bohm as early as 1950 and to which Ali and Das developed a quantum correction term. The model would remove the need for dark energy.

The problem with the Big Bang theory is its contradiction with the general theory of relativity; the laws of physics do not seem to apply the closer we go to the Big Bang.

English philosopher and metaphysician J.M.E. McTaggart, who suggested in his book *The Unreality of Time* (1908) that time is not real, states:

> Experience provides one kind of indubitable knowledge: knowledge by acquaintance of our own inner states. Any theory about the world that fails to explain how our inner states can arise is inadequate.

In combining theories, therefore, one must also take into account the mind and consciousness. Since the prevailing view is still that consciousness is the result of brain activity, the mind and consciousness are usually completely ignored as a topic. They are considered to belong more to metaphysics.

I mentioned the seminar I attended when I started writing this chapter. In particular, I was interested to hear whether consciousness and its place in physical theories would emerge in the seminar. Indeed, several presentations raised the need for a theory that would also explain the movements of the mind.

Physicist Tuomo Suntola gave a lecture at the seminar about his suggestion for a unified theory. Dr. Suntola received the 2018 Millennium Technology Prize for his technology of atomic layer deposition (ALD) that enables manufacturing of nanoscale thin material layers for microprocessors and digital memory devices. But his work related to the theory of everything hasn't received much publicity so far. Maybe the reason for this is that Suntola suggests an alternative theory. The other reason may be that the approach is physical and it is difficult to interpret what the theory really means. I am thus, interested to hear more about the theory, since now the topic is also being approached from the view of philosophy.

Suntola considers the biggest challenge for the natural sciences at the moment to be to close the gap between metaphysics and empiricism and to find a theory that connects different theories and forms an understandable picture of reality. We have moved from one extreme to the other, when measurements often lack a philosophical basis. In Suntola's model one moves from observer-centered thinking to systems-centered thinking.

Suntola's Dynamic Universe (DU) theory is a holistic description of the observable physical universe, and combines the most essential features of relativity theory and quantum physics. In DU's view on reality there is absolute time and space. The world is modeled in four dimensions, where the fourth dimension is space's own motion, that is, its expansion. Space is a closed four-dimensional spherical surface that acts like a pendulum. It receives energy from its own gravity during the contraction phase and, as it expands, releases it back into the energy of gravity. Thus, instead of Einstein's three space dimensions and time, DU has four space dimensions, where the fourth dimension describes the motion of expansion at the speed of light in the universe. If the structure of the universe is a spherical surface and you go anywhere on the surface of the sphere, you will never come to its boundary or edge, yet it is bounded and finite. So the 3D space we experience could very well be the surface of a four-dimensional sphere. The fourth dimension is present, but we do not notice it, as I pointed out in the previous chapter on dimensions.

It would seem, however, that the DU fails to address the most important point to which I sought an answer and which would be needed to build a true unified theory. DU as a physical theory does not consider consciousness and its location. The mind and body are theoretically treated as a single entity guided by the universal laws of nature. The phenomena, which we call spiritual, thus come into consideration in theory, for they are not detached from the whole, but are thought to come from the same oneness. However, DU has features suggestive of panpsychism, as mass, according to DU, is not just a property of objects, but the foundation of everything, even the foundation of our existence. It is an abstract quality that cannot be seen unless it is energized. It is, thus, the hidden foundation behind everything. Energy does not necessarily manifest as mass, but can also be in a finer form, which also allows for mentally considered phenomena. One could make an interpretation of DU that would explain spirituality as an interaction of energies.

In contrast to theories so far, in which the universe has been seen as an empty space filled with discrete particles, DU's notion is that the universe with its laws is a four-dimensional self-organizing and flexible entity in which change and motion are continuous. In fact, it mathematically describes the abstract forms of the world outlined by Plato, the philosophy of ideas, and the essence of matter. The world we perceive was created based on an original model when it was projected into a formless state. *Materia prima*, or the formless state on which matter is based, cannot exist as such, but manifests itself after receiving energy when two opposites unite. Perhaps everything in this theory will gradually lead to consciousness as the basis of everything?

DU is an interesting approach to describing reality, as it combines experimental knowledge, existing theories, and Eastern wisdom as well. Nor does it rule out our own impact. In her article interpreting DU, Dr. Tarja Kallio-Tamminen states that DU allows for our influence on reality. Our intention creates a new kind of form among the existing possibilities, that is, the potential becomes reality. Therefore, we inevitably have to start thinking about our ethical responsibility for what we bring to real form. Perhaps one of DU's essential messages to the world lies in this: We are part of a whole and relevant to the formation of reality.

Suntola mentioned in his presentation the need for a paradigm shift. I agree that it is needed, although Suntola, to my understanding, refers to the physical approach proposed in DU that differs from existing theories. However, DU would not seem to rule out the role of consciousness as fundamental, although it emphasizes the importance of matter. In any case, it has been noted from many perspectives that current theories alone do not work and a new approach is needed. The different approaches that shake the prevailing thinking, which seek to take into account the shortcomings of current theories, seem to be the rule of this era rather than the exception. The seminar I attended also showed this. I have dealt with many of these different approaches in this book.

What is needed is a real *all-inclusive theory*, a theory of the whole cosmos, which would encompass everything related to existence, not only the physical dimension, but also the mental, the spiritual; it would also account for consciousness. Understanding the connection between science and spirituality, and also dealing with spirituality through the means of science, is necessary before a theory of everything can ever come about.

We currently live in the time of a paradigm shift, a time of change like that of the 17th century.

CHAPTER 12
CHANGING WORLDVIEW

The notion that science and spirituality are somehow mutually exclusive does a disservice to both.

—Carl Sagan

From time to time I organize group remote healing sessions, where hundreds of people participate. In my healing sessions, at a scheduled time, the healees participate wherever they are, remotely, often even thousands of miles away. Most of the time I don't know anything about my healees except their first names. I wrote down the following lines after one remote healing session:

> *I remained listening to my feelings and what changed when the treatment started. I felt a huge amount of 'noise.' It's hard to explain because it wasn't a sound. It was more of a feeling, as if many would have spoken at the same time, a focus on something else. I had a feeling that I went to pick up each one of the healees individually for the treatment. Gradually the noise subsided and only a strong presence remained. I had a feeling that we were all there together. Everyone had a reason to participate, and together we strengthened each other. There seemed to be an enormous force; it's hard to explain that.*

The feeling of presence that I have experienced in the group remote healing sessions is something extraordinary. As I experience it, I have a feeling that I can never be alone. We really have a connection to each other, we are one, and that connection is also possible to experience.

Ten years ago, I wouldn't have understood this, but now it is an everyday reality for me. And it's not in contradiction with science, even though I might not have understood it at the time.

The more we face anomalies, experiences that we cannot explain, the more our worldview is shaken. As each one of us gradually changes our thinking, so does the prevailing worldview. Gradually, it will also lead to a paradigm shift.

The 20th-century American philosopher Thomas Kuhn created the concept of paradigm shift, which described the fundamental changes in concepts and experimental practices that take place in science from time to time. According to Kuhn, a paradigm shift is a scientific revolution in which old science and methodology are replaced by new ones. The paradigm shift in its broadest meaning is, then, a change in the prevailing worldview. The change is often preceded by a period of stagnation, when new theories and approaches are knocked out, even if they are well-founded. All indications are that we are living in such a time right now in terms of science and spirituality, body and mind. Science and spirituality are not opposing views, but different perspectives on the same entity. Sri Sri Ravi Shankar says in Taavi Kassila's book *Meeting with the Masters* that science and spirituality are intertwined, as both are a driven by a desire to know. Science asks, *"what is this?"* and spirituality in turn *"who am I?"*

The theory of everything must be able to discover the answer to human existence and include spirituality, which also means solving the question of consciousness. Reality is basically always both material and spiritual, as we currently define it. In every case and at every level, matter and spirit exist at the same time. We have gradually moved from one extreme to the other: As technology has evolved with materialism and the understanding of matter in the Western world has increased, the connection to spirituality has narrowed.

However, there is no model of our physical world that is a *real* description of the world, of reality. All are just *our experiences* of the physical world. Therefore, the most important thing that can be done in science is to try to understand the spiritual side of reality. We must make an effort to understand perception as well as experience.

Johanna Blomqvist

Spiritual reality

Quantum physics restored to science the mental side that had been neglected for decades, even hundreds of years. What does quantum physics mean to our understanding of reality?

The fact that quantum mechanics does not describe the particle world itself, but *our knowledge* of this world, is already a challenging change. It means that in addition to the matter that quantum mechanics describes, reality has mental or spiritual features. This is still difficult to admit in science, as it would mean a paradigm shift. Many interpretations of quantum physics have sought to explain it in a way that preserves some of the most important features of classical physics, such as determinism and causality, and to eliminate many of the oddities of quantum physics.

Knowledge involves consciousness that produces knowledge. When examining observations and the process involved, we must also account for the free will of the observer: The choice of the method of observation sometimes has a decisive effect on the properties of the system under study. Doing science is not possible without free will. Therefore, the materialistic conception of reality that still prevails in physics and science more broadly is not sufficient. Throughout the 20th century and early 2000s, the inadequacy of materialism has been ignored in physics and science, because materialism has enabled tremendous technological development. There has been no need to consider the adequacy of the model and its ability to describe reality, and the actual difficulty of describing reality has been avoided by accepting realism and leaving philosophy to philosophers. Quantum physics is accepted as the most successful current theory, as all its predictions have proved to be true one after another. It is therefore strange that physicists have avoided reflection on the philosophical problems associated with it. It has been easier to ignore some of the most peculiar features of the Copenhagen interpretation, for example, in order to avoid problems. It has been easier to rule out the spiritual side and ignore the deep philosophical problems that remained in the minds of the developers of the theories. This attitude has inevitably influenced the development of science based on these theories. For example, problems arising from the fact that it is not possible to distinguish between what is observed and the effect of the observer or of the rest of the environment have been ignored. However, we know the observer and environment have an effect, such as in placebo or randomized double-blind trials, which nonetheless are widely used in medicine even for evaluation. In practice, it is not possible to distinguish between the two groups, at least not very easily.

Quantum physics has taught us something new about reality. Unlike classical physics, at the particle level we cannot reach reality with our senses or with experimental methods in general. The best understanding of particle-level reality can be obtained through a description of quantum mechanics that cannot be compared to "Self-reality." That is the primordial one world, which I will explain more below. This is what Bohr called complementarity and Heisenberg uncertainty, and it makes it virtually impossible to reach "Self-reality." Reality cannot be described in detail by rational theory, for reality seems to be blurred when one tries to accurately describe it. In the Copenhagen interpretation, this basic situation was seen as a new feature of reality, not, therefore, an indication that our knowledge of reality was in some way incomplete.

Quantum physics also reveals a feature about reality, which is familiar from Eastern philosophies: It is not possible to distinguish the object and the observer from each other; instead they form an indivisible whole. The world of matter and the world of spirit exploring the former are one. Physics is thus returning to a closer connection between matter and spirit. What is needed is a new kind of model, and a paradigm shift. The "soul" has for centuries not been a part of physics, but now it is returning back to science. In the future, this elapsed period will be viewed in the same way as the 17th century is now, as a necessary stage in development, but one-sided, as if we had only looked at the other side of the object (see e.g. the cylinder image of reality in Figure 1 in this book), and moved from one extreme to the other.

At the time of the birth of quantum physics, there were several physicists pondering the underlying philosophy and what it all really means. According to Wolfgang Pauli, quantum physics gradually leads to a notion that reality  can never be elucidated by rational scientific methods. Science, religion and spirituality merge together. The complementarity of quantum mechanics gave Pauli the idea to approach the mind and body problem. He thought that physical and mental phenomena are complementary to each other, in the same way that waveform and particle image are in quantum theory. In their discussions, Pauli and Jung came to the idea of an abstract one world, which they called Unus Mundus, an idea close to Plato's "that which really is." Unus Mundus is not illustratively descriptive, but manifests itself to us as either physical phenomena or spiritual experiences. The term Unus Mundus came originally from the 16th-century German physician and alchemist Gerhard Dorn. Pauli attached to this one-world concept the idea of the complementarity of the physical and mental aspects of reality. In quantum mechanics, complementarity arises from the combination of discreteness and continuity: The totality of these opposites gives rise to a reality that includes both the rational and the irrational side.

Pauli describes the "Self-reality," primordial one world, presented in Figure 11, as consisting of three dimensions: physical and mental experiences, in addition to which there are irrational dimensions. By irrational dimensions, Pauli means dimensions the rational worldview of science cannot reach. Pauli's view was that they can only be reached by faith. According to him, the division of science and religion in the 17th century, after which science undertook to understand matter and the church the intangible world, should not have been made. It is impossible for science to find an explanation for all observations with current methods: A complete description of individual events is not possible by scientific means. As a result, the scientific perspective on reality also inevitably remains transcendent – unattainable.

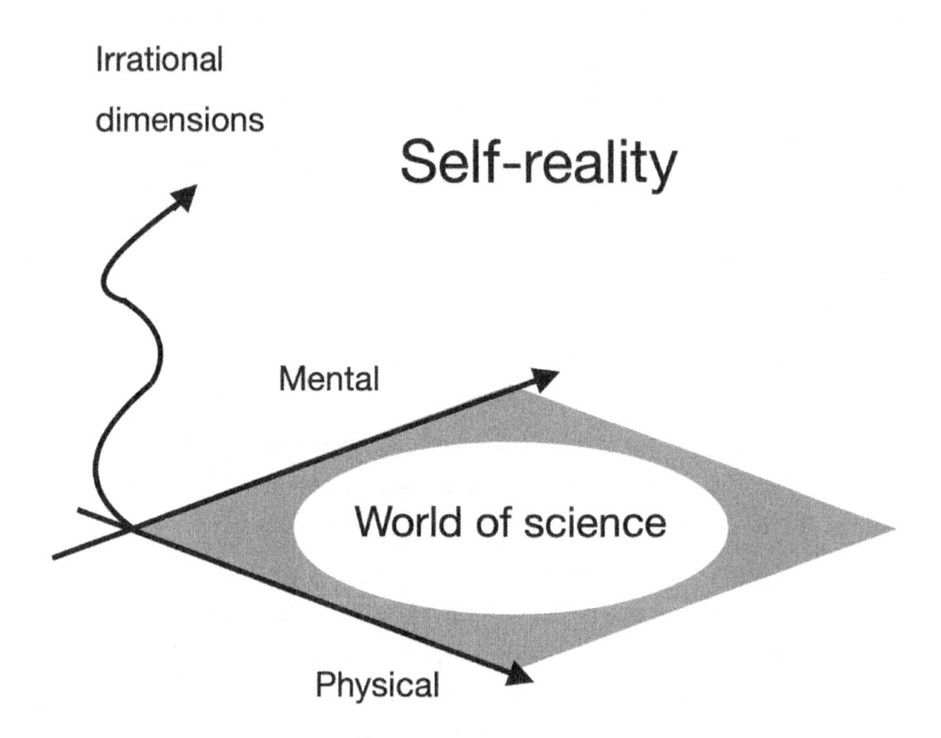

FIGURE 11. WOLFGANG PAULI'S "SELF-REALITY" [FROM THE DISSERTATION OF K.V. LAURIKAINEN].

"Self-reality" is the foundation of our existence. It has something for each one of us that suits our own worldview. Self-reality is God, Allah, Yahweh, the Source of Everything or something else. Everything comes from the same origin. There is not only one true view, but all see the same foundation of existence that is impossible to achieve with reason. God is transcendent, but at the same time immanent, influential in the world we experience. It is a higher power that we cannot explain.

If the idea of complementarity were extended to this, one cannot even distinguish between the creator and the created. We are an indivisible whole, unity.

Anomalies, or phenomena that cannot be explained using the prevailing science, are dismissed as impossible, as a product of mind or classified as belonging to the field of parapsychology. They are mysteries for science, but perhaps because they have a dimension that the current model of science is unable to explain. The objective physical world and the subjective spiritual world intersect. We ourselves are the best manifestation of "Self-reality," a reference to the fact that everything comes from the same source, the same origin, as all other phenomena. Maybe we are constantly connected to that source, the field, sometimes more consciously, sometimes unconsciously? Maybe creativity and intuition also emerge from there? Maybe from time to time, for example in dreams or through meditation and other exercises, we can achieve a better connection to this field?

We need a view on reality where science and spirituality unite. This would not be only a mathematical solution, a model merging all theories and interactions, but a comprehensive change of thinking. It is necessary to understand the world and its phenomena. We also need it to understand ourselves and our own place in the universe, in reality.

A model merging science and spirituality

Reality cannot be considered only as material. Reality consists of both physical and mental aspects. Our own subjective experiences are needed to understand the world and they bring a spiritual aspect to reality.

Consciousness plays a significant role in science and spirituality. The collapse of the wave function under the influence of an observer in quantum physics can be interpreted as caused by the consciousness of the observer. It was originally thought that quantum physics would strengthen materialism, but it so happened that with quantum physics, classical physics and materialism came into great difficulty. Our reality is more peculiar than we would think, and we seem to have a special significance in it.

The fear of many physicists may have been that if the role of consciousness is found to be more fundamental than matter, many laws of physics would not work anymore – and we would return to the era of superstition. The chief scientist of IONS (Institute of Noetic Sciences) Dean Radin presents a model that shows this is most likely not the case. Classical physics and the material world can be seen as special cases of quantum physics, and there is thus no need to change the existing theories. There is no need to abandon classical physics, since it describes everyday-level phenomena well. Only the interrelationship between different disciplines should be considered.

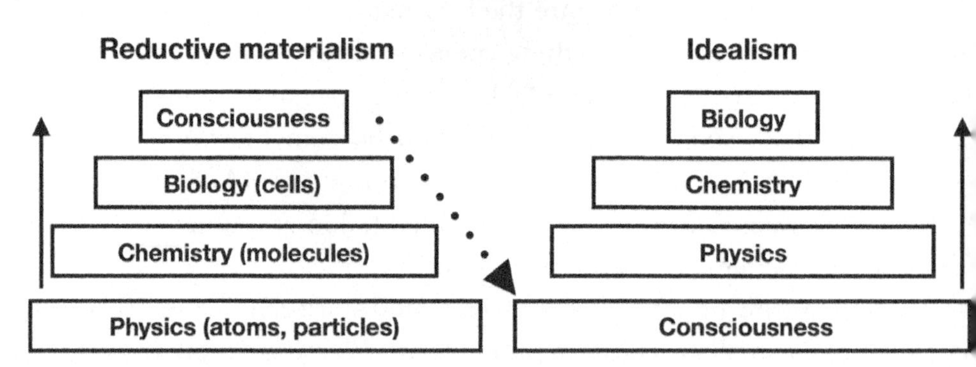

FIGURE 12. THE LOCATION OF CONSCIOUSNESS IN REDUCTIVE MATERIALISM AND IN IDEALISM. THE DIRECTION OF THE ARROW DESCRIBES THE EMERGENCE AND CAUSE-EFFECT RELATIONSHIP (CAUSATION). THE ARROW MARKED WITH THE DOTTED LINE SHOWS HOW THE PLACE OF CONSCIOUSNESS CHANGES IN MODELS.

Figure 12 shows the connections between different disciplines, according to the current view of reductive materialism. Different disciplines describe different levels of reality. Physics is seen as the basis of everything. Atoms and particles are thought of as the basic units of the entire material world. Atoms together form molecules that need chemistry to be described. Increasingly larger systems, such as cells, are described by biology. Scientists have usually focused on their own specialty, as few physicists are even familiar with chemistry, let alone biology.

Consciousness is seen as a product of the brain, and there is actually no meaning for consciousness, and it is seen only as an illusion. From this point of view, the idea that the mind, for example, could influence matter is difficult, if not impossible. There are many interesting theories to explain consciousness on this basis, including the theory based on microtubules developed by Stuart Hameroff and Roger Penrose, which I discussed earlier, in the chapter on consciousness.

In the model's left side, then, the particle level is the basis of everything, and from which everything begins to form, but on the right, everything is based on consciousness. This right-side model can be called idealistic and monistic. Consciousness is followed by physics, and then chemistry and biology. David Bohm's theory of implicit order is an example of this. Bohm saw the world as essentially a mental rather than a physical creation. Bernardo Kastrup's DIH model, which I mentioned in the chapter on consciousness, is another example of an idealistic model. These models make it much easier to understand influencing physical reality. Consciousness is not dependent on space-time. If there is no space-time as in classical physics, for example, it is easier to understand that subjective, mental-level experiences such as ESP, telepathy, and remote viewing can be explained with this model. Consciousness also creates a subjective mental level.

It is also much easier to explain some of the exceptional forms of knowing using the idealistic model. Einstein, for example, had rather typical grades, and he didn't show any particularly exceptional talent, yet in just a few years he developed his world-revolutionary theory of relativity. Einstein is often even spoken of as a genius, just like Leonardo da Vinci or Mozart. They have all described the birth of their creations as if they had fallen from heaven upon them. All they had to do was write down the ready-made model that was already in their mind.

Exceptionally astonishing forms of knowing are evident in so-called savants. Dr. Diane Hennacy Powell has studied autistic children, including a 5-year old boy named Ramses who was capable of doing astounding calculations. It turned out that Ramses, in fact, was able to do telepathy and to read answers from his questioner's mind. There are also other interesting forms of savant talent, such as the cases where the person suddenly has exceptional talents after an accident, like starting to speak a foreign language, even a language they have never spoken or learned.

None of these cases can be explained using the materialistic model. The assumption of consciousness as the basis of everything also changes our perspective on where a phenomenon is observed. Such phenomena as intuition, the effect of mind, manifestation or intention and, for example, energy healing have to be observed from an entirely new basis.

We thus have to turn our thinking upside down, since all evidence points in the direction that our consciousness, our mind, actively affects the reality we observe. We are continually manifesting the future, often unconsciously. Even our thoughts matter. We should thus take responsibility for our own influence on reality.

A growing number of scholars has recently begun to lean in the direction of the idealistic model. Besides Radin, Bohm and Kastrup, the topic has been raised by such scholars as Stuart Kauffman (*Humanity in a Creative Universe*), Charles T. Tart (*The End of Materialism: How Evidence of the Paranormal Is Bringing Science and Spirit Together*), Robert C. Koons (*The Waning of Materialism*), Thomas Nagel (*Mind and Cosmos: Why the Materialist Neo-Darwinian Conception of Nature Is Almost Certainly False*) and E. Kelly, A. Crabtree and P. Marshall (*Beyond Physicalism*). The transition to the so-called post-materialistic era is considered an even more significant shift in human history than the transition from a geocentric to a heliocentric worldview was. A change in mindset is also seen as necessary for human survival.

The manifesto

A growing number of scholars agree that it is time to abandon materialism. It's time to move on. Several hundred scholars, professors, and influencers in the sciences have signed a manifesto to emphasize the importance of the transition, bringing together the most important points about what is at stake and what is needed for change. The manifesto calls for a complete upheaval of the current scientific worldview based on classical physics and materialism. During the 20th century, this ideology became so prevalent that for many scholars, the approach is self-evident and the only one possible: Matter is the only reality and the mind is seen as the output of the brain, although this cannot be explained.

Scientific materialism has been necessary, for without it technology would not be at the point it is now. Few of us want to go back in time before all this technology, and there is no need. The technology has also brought with it a lot of freedom. However, the manifesto highlights the fact that it is only one side of the whole: Matter is only the other side of reality, nor should materialism shackle science and research, as has been the case with consciousness and mind-related subjective phenomena. As a result of materialism, the understanding of subjective experiences has been almost ignored. Partly subjective experiences have also been studied under parapsychology.

Science should be an objective, impartial, and transparent means of acquiring knowledge and studying and explaining things, and, as the manifesto states, the methods and approaches of science should not reflect any particular belief, dogma or ideology, but be impartial.

The manifesto also sets out reasons why we should pay attention to understanding experiences and experientialism right now. Phenomena that could not be explained by classical physics and that formed the basis for the development of quantum physics originally came from the realm of physics. Research in quantum physics has shown that our material world is made up of atoms and particles, which are also not matter, solid objects, and for which the exact location or time cannot be determined. Above all, quantum mechanics showed a connection between the observer and the observable.

There are studies that have found that sometimes, in certain situations, we can obtain relevant information without our ordinary senses by means that are not explained by our current understanding of space and time. There can be a connection between us even at distances. As I have described in this book, remote influencing of machines and living systems, including humans, is possible. These phenomena are so common that they cannot be considered anomalies; instead, we should learn to understand them. They speak to significant occurrences that are impossible to explain through materialism.

Manifesto for a post-materialist science in this new era (see references for more details):

a) Mind represents an aspect of reality as primordial as the physical world is presumed to be. Mind cannot be derived from matter and reduced to anything more basic.

b) There is a deep interconnectedness between mind and the physical world.
c) Mind (will/intention) can influence the state of the physical world. The phenomenon is not confined to specific points in space, nor to specific points in time, such as the present. Since the mind may non-locally influence the physical world, the intentions, emotions, and desires of an experimenter may not be completely isolated from experimental outcomes, even in controlled and blinded experimental designs.
d) Minds are apparently unbounded and may unite in ways suggesting a unitary One Mind that includes all individual, single minds.
e) The mind can work through the brain, but is not produced by it. Near-death experience (NDE) in cardiac arrest suggests this. NDE coupled with evidence from research mediums further suggest the survival of consciousness following bodily death and the existence of other non-physical levels of reality.
f) Scientists should not be afraid to investigate spirituality and spiritual experiences since they represent a central aspect of human existence.

It is necessary for us to move to the next level, to the post-materialistic era. We don't have any alternatives, if we want to continue our life as humanity on Earth into the future. We have to change our thinking, which is not necessarily the easiest task, but the time is most conducive to this change, for change has already begun in many ways. Climate change has brought value and relevance, as well as an ethical dimension, to the debate. Materialism supports the old thinking associated with consumer society, the pursuit of economic growth, the importance of money, and the pursuit of one's own wealth and support of the ego. However, so many stories that can be considered success stories in terms of materialism have shown that reality is something else. Man does not become happy through material wealth, as true wealth is somewhere else.

Nature can no longer withstand materialism; we have no options. The amount of plastic on the planet is still increasing, even though many countries have already begun to look for ways to remedy the situation by banning plastic bags, among other things. Clean water is available to only a small portion of the world's population, and often that too is unknowingly saturated with chemicals and drug residues. We can no longer dispose of plastic, chemicals and toxins in nature and think it doesn't affect us, because we are part of the whole. It is necessary to change our thinking and see the big picture.

In my mind, I return to my childhood, and how I imagined the world to work. I often heard that it is like winning a lottery to be born in Finland, and how well we all live, but I couldn't understand why things would be different elsewhere. It didn't fit in my thinking as a child. I wondered: Why, then, don't we help others? How could all be right for me if it is not for a child in Ethiopia, for how could one child be more important than another? I believe that a paradigm shift will also change the way we see ourselves and our role in the world. We are all one. What you do to others will also return back to you. Values such as goodness, compassion, love, trust, honesty, and peace prevail in the new paradigm.

CHAPTER 13
REALITY IS...

Reality is what we take to be true. What we take to be true is what we believe. What we believe determines what we take to be true. What we take to be true is our reality.

—David Bohm

In this book I have presented several different views on reality, some thousands of years old, some newer, some more science based, some less. While reality may seem inaccessible behind the veil of our senses and understanding at first, there is something we have learned and know about it. Before continuing further, I gather together here some observations on reality, what we know about it and its features.

- **Reality is something other than our experience of it.** There is a reality, or a model of reality, that we are unable to reach with our experiences. Maybe we can say that reality is quantized? Quantification is a means of roughly examining things by partitioning them, rather than seeing them as a continuity, which leads to the assumption that only certain states are possible. The primal reality contains all possible alternatives, but due to our limited comprehension, perhaps we can perceive only a certain reality?
- **We are unable to reach the primal reality.** However, we are able to understand that we cannot comprehend it. The universe, where we are, is part of reality, but not necessarily the whole reality.
- **There are different levels of reality.** We are able to make a connection to these levels by different means, and none of these levels is more profound than another. Together they form our understanding of

reality. For example, with our vision we receive a different feeling of the surroundings than we do with meditation.

- **Reality is both physical and mental.** These different aspects are connected to each other. Consciousness affects physical reality.
- **Reality is irrational.** Therefore, it cannot be understood only through the rational means of science.
- **There are phenomena that are independent of time and place.** Consciousness is independent of time and non-local.
- **Time and space do not really exist.** Time is an experience created by our limited comprehension of the perceived order of events. Space is also a creation of our quantized ability to perceive.
- **Complementarity is a feature of reality.** Opposites don't cancel each other out, but together form the whole. Just like light: Although we know that it is particles, this doesn't exclude the fact that light is also waves.
- **Freedom exists in reality, at least within certain limits.** We are part of reality and active influencers of reality.
- **There is statistical causality in reality.** The future of a single event cannot be predicted with certainty, but the behavior of a large group obeys causality.

Would it be possible to combine all these to one common model of the world?

CHAPTER 14
REALITY IS… A SIMULATION

> *Have you ever had a dream, Neo, that you were so sure was real? What if you were unable to wake from that dream, Neo? How would you know the difference between the dream world and the real world?*
>
> —Morpheus to Neo in *The Matrix*

I had a dream that was so clear, it was as if I was awake. As it ended I returned back to my bedroom, and I saw my body there below; I was looking at it from the ceiling of the room. I had a feeling that I know everything and I am able to move wherever I want just by thinking. I knew it was 8:40 AM and it was time to wake up. I also knew how my day would continue: what would happen, who I would meet, what we would talk about and so on. It felt as if I was creating my forthcoming day before waking up. My dream ended and I felt I was dropping into my body… When I woke up, I kept my eyes closed for a while and – no matter how much I wanted to remember – I almost completely forgot my sleep, except for the last part of the dream I described above. I remembered particularly well the feeling of how I felt in my sleep, how my body started to restrict my movements, my thoughts, all my activities, and I was no longer free. I opened my eyes, and it was 8:40, of course.

After waking up, I kept wondering: *How can I be sure that I am not dreaming right now? What in fact is real? What if the dream were true and I could constantly create the future? What if what we call dream is really the true, primal reality? Are we experiencing only a small part of that when we are awake? Are we actually living as avatars in a simulation?*

Simulated reality?

In his philosophical treatise *Meditations on First Philosophy* René Descartes pondered the question of whether we humans might constantly be in a dream instead of being awake. How can we be sure that we are not always dreaming? Our senses are unreliable, and we can't trust them, if we want to understand what reality truly is. We cannot rely solely on even the rational means of science, for the means of present science do not reach the irrational part of reality.

I saw a video from a country where computers are a rarity. There was an event organized on one city street, where people had an opportunity to try virtual glasses and virtual reality. In the video, virtual glasses were placed on one man's head, and the virtual reality program was launched. The man was astonished. He threw the glasses off his head and jumped from the chair really fast, rolling his eyes, he was so surprised. The virtual reality had felt so real that he was shocked. Virtual reality seemed to be real for him, so it was simulated reality. One can usually easily recognize that virtual reality is artificial, but due to technological development we are approaching the "true" reality, and it is more and more difficult to distinguish real from simulation. What if we are even now living in a simulated reality, but are unable to notice the difference?

If the virtual reality were well made, it might even be that we are living in a simulated reality produced by someone else and we don't even notice.

In the new version of *Jumanji*, the movie, four teens disappear into Jumanji world as avatars. They thus start living as game characters. The foursome have to play sometimes dangerous Jumanji games until the finish to get out of the game; otherwise they will be stuck inside the game forever.

How do we know even today that we are not living our lives in the same way, as avatars in a game?

One difference from *Jumanji* is that in our "game" we have, presumably, only one life to live, while in *Jumanji* each had three lives.

Sometimes the possibility of a simulation is questioned by suggesting that it would be easy to test: If everything was just an illusion, then, for example, when walking in front of a train, nothing should happen. However, this is not the case. The experiences in the simulation are real. The simulation may well be completely real and you may also die in it.

Perhaps one of the best-known films made on the simulation hypothesis is the Matrix movie series. In the Matrix, people live as slaves to machines but experience a very different reality from what they actually live: "*If real is what you can feel, smell, taste and see, then real is simply electrical signals interpreted by your brain.*"

Bernardo Kastrup writes in his book *The Idea of the World*: "*If all reality is in consciousness, then the world is akin to a dream.*" I am convinced that consciousness is fundamental to the manifestation of reality. If consciousness creates our physical reality, then maybe we really do live in a dream or a simulation?

I have to admit that I had already long ago abandoned the hypothesis that our reality could be a simulation. The simulation hypothesis is usually considered a materialistic way to explain reality: It is thought that there would be technology, perhaps created by some more advanced civilization than ours, and the reality we're experiencing and we ourselves would just be a simulation running on a massive supercomputer. We may only be imagining we are real and alive, but in reality we are just moving bits. However, a materialistic simulation such as this does not explain consciousness or free will any better than other materialistic approaches. What if we think that reality is a simulation created by consciousness? In fact, the simulation hypothesis allows for both monistic idealism and monistic materialism, and it is not necessary even to take a position on what creates the simulation.

This option started to interest me even more due to the fact that in the early 2000s, I worked for almost 10 years at a supercomputer center as a specialist and development manager. Maybe this too is synchronicity?

Is reality a simulation created by consciousness?

The development of computers in recent decades has been astounding, making it possible to simulate more and more complex physical systems and processes with unprecedented, ever-improving accuracy and power. While the possibility of simulation may sound like science fiction, it certainly no longer sounds as impossible as it might have in the 1950s, when the first computers were newly developed and a very rudimentary computer still filled an entire room. Now, we've begun to understand for example how enormous the power extremely small quantum computers could have. While I am writing these lines, in the fall of 2019, Google announced that it had developed a quantum computer that took just 3 minutes and 20 seconds to perform the calculation that would have taken 10,000 years for the most powerful computer to date. It no longer seems impossible at all to think of a simulation that has been going on for 13.77 billion years, and in this time brought about this kind of reality where we live currently.

Let's assume, then, that the physical reality we observe is a simulation created by consciousness. The simulation is like a computer game, just like Minecraft. Someone has planned and created Minecraft, but for us the creator of the game does not appear. In the same way we could assume that the simulation where we are also has a creator, which we call consciousness, creator, oneness or some other name suitable for us.

Consciousness is fundamental, and is all that exists, including us. The simulation of physical reality is projected from our consciousness, just like movies in cinemas. What we observe really exists for us, but it is at the same time a simulation – a "real" simulation, just as the virtual reality was for the man I mentioned at the beginning of this chapter, who tried virtual glasses for the first time.

The consciousness simulation would explain one essential challenge which we have not been able to explain. That is the flow of information. Brian Whitworth from Massey University, New Zealand articulates the challenge in his book, *The Physical World as a Virtual Reality*, this way:

> How can every electron, quark, and in fact every point in space seem to know its function? These smallest parts of the universe have no mechanism to make decisions by themselves. However, if the world is thought to be virtual reality, the problem disappears.

I pondered this same question earlier in this book when I discussed morphic fields and how, for example, an animal's fur "knows" when to change color. The information has to be in some sort of a field to which they all have access.

In my book *From Quantum Physics to Energy Healing,* I suggested that instead of the term *"energy"* one should use *"information." "Energy"* doesn't correctly describe the phenomenon we are dealing with. I consider the forming of the connection as one of the main focal points in energy healing, and via that receiving the information and channeling it. Maybe the basis of the nature of reality relies on information? Whitworth suggests that matter, charge, energy and motion are all different sides of information and also that all conservational laws would in fact be laws related to the conservation of information.

One argument for the centrality of information can be found by considering the behavior of light. The behavior of light can be explained based on quantum mechanics, that is the behavior of photons, as a reflection from the surface of the sea obeys certain probabilities. For example, instead of saying every fourth photon would reflect, we would say out of all photons, 25% reflect from the surface. It is impossible to know out of 100 photons, which ones reflect and how a single photon behaves; one can only say how the whole group of photons together behaves. Twenty-five percent of all photons reflect. Photons seem to know where all other photons are and behave accordingly. But how can they know? Photons are all identical, that is a single photon has no reason to behave differently than others. This phenomenon is also real at the level of everyday life, not just at the level of particles. For example, what is it that connects the photons reflected from the surface of the sea, the sea surface, us observers and our consciousness? The wave doctrine cannot explain this, nor can the flow of information be explained through a cause-and-effect relationship. However, if information and simulation are considered as the basis of everything, a software algorithm would have no problem in dealing with such behavior. Photons must have access to the same information. Almost all phenomena in quantum physics are of this nature in practice.

With the simulation hypothesis it would also be possible to combine and explain the topics discussed earlier in this book. If we are living in a simulation created by consciousness, what is the nature of consciousness? The topic has been discussed widely; besides Whitworth, philosopher Nick Boström from the University of Oxford and physicist Bernard Haisch from Calphysics Institute consider consciousness as simulation. Haisch raises some interesting questions, which I have extended further in the following. Maybe our reality truly is a simulation?

The universe was at first only a small dot. Why did it expand?

It is natural that a simulation needs to begin from somewhere. We can find analogies, for example, in Minecraft or Sims. In the beginning, there is nothing, until we start building. There is only a certain framework for implementing the game and following the rules of the game. In the same way as in a game, the universe could well have started with the creation of frameworks, laws of nature, within which the simulation functions. The current simulation has been going on for about 13.77 billion years. During that time, the simulation can grow from the point tremendously.

Why was the universe born?

If reality is virtual the explanation is natural: All simulations sometimes need to be "booted," i.e. restarted, reset. Maybe there was an update that needed to be implemented?

In reality are we one?

We have to be one. How else would information flow immediately in some situations? In a physical world, we have to get used to handling and considering physical objects and even ourselves as separate from everything. The assumption of separation is, however, needed only for computational reasons. In practice that is not the case. We are one through consciousness and through that we have access to the same information.

Who are we?

We are "players," avatars, in the simulation. Just as in a game, there are other "players" in the world, which are active influencers in our life and also passive, like statistics, who have no real impact in our life.

What is time?

The events of the simulation are like frames of a movie. The movie can be played at different speeds; the theory of relativity explains this among other things. Time is different for different players. Since we are all, however, "players" in the simulation of the same consciousness, our experience of time is almost identical. Time is how we experience the simulation model. Time is a result of our limited comprehension.

Does free will exist?

There are settings in the simulation that are pre-set, like frames within which the simulation starts to function, and which we cannot influence. However, part we can decide ourselves. We can thus influence the simulation we are. We have free will within certain limits.

Is it possible to get out of the simulation?

Getting out of the simulation means breaking away from the grip of physicality, matter and conscious mind. Perhaps silencing the conscious mind, meditating, works best by closing the eyes and ears, because it is comparable to taking virtual glasses away from the head? This could also explain why many autistic children have special abilities. Maybe in cases like this, "virtual glasses" aren't really on at all?

What is death?

In the Star Trek television series, on the starship Enterprise people sometimes experienced a *"holodeck"* stage, which was a state before moving to a new world. Maybe death is like a transition from this world to *"holodeck,"* before we move to a new life, a new simulation? Perhaps that is also why we can return to previous lives in some situations, for example in hypnosis, dreams, or other transformed states of consciousness. We can thus receive information from other simulations as well. When a new simulation begins, a new life starts, and we can choose that in *holodeck*.

Why are there such limits as the speed of light and Planck length?

The speed of light, which is the upper limit of speed, could be an indication of the maximum processing speed of the physical simulation. However, in such phenomena where consciousness is involved, there is no upper limit, but the knowledge is transferred immediately. Such phenomena are entanglement, energy healing, remote viewing, telepathy, and intuition, for example.

Planck length, the smallest possible dimension, could in turn be a measure of the accuracy of the simulation, which therefore means the "pixel size" of the simulation.

How are non-local instantaneous effects possible for entangled particles?

Separation is computational, not real. It is possible to access the information immediately.

Why are there phenomena that are quantized? Why are there discrete state transitions in quantum mechanics?

This could be a natural phenomenon for digital simulation.

Could machines become conscious?

Yes, but not in the same way as we are. We are "part of consciousness," out of which we are created and simulated. Awareness that mimics consciousness can be built on machines, as in current games, but machines can't be conscious in the same way as we are. Unless one is able to organize a way for consciousness to steer the machine, to create a new "controller." However, it can hardly happen, at least from the level of the simulation, unless there are already initially such connections programmed to the simulation (brain?).

According to Bernardo Kastrup, to create a conscious being, we have to be able to produce a dissociation in the cosmic mind. We are all "mirrors," parts dissociated from the cosmic mind, and the connection to cosmic mind has to be created to be able to create a conscious being. This means a new player, or soul, not a machine as avatar. Could a soul separated from the body possibly steer that kind of a machine?

Can simulation theory connect quantum mechanics and the theory of relativity?

Simulation theory could connect Einstein's theory of relativity and quantum theory, and thus the theory of relativity would explain how space-time was created, and quantum theory how energy and matter are born. Suntola's DU theory and the simulation hypothesis also seem compatible.

What is the consciousness that creates reality? Who runs the simulation?

This is the question we have tried to answer for thousands of years. There is no theory that has found an adequate answer. The simulation hypothesis would provide answers to many questions previous theories could not, and it would also be able to explain the role of consciousness. This consciousness could be Plato's "That which really is," Oneness, God, Source, Brahman and so on behind everything. All these names lead to one and the same; they are creations of humans and represent what holds and controls the whole. It is only possible to conceptualize the creator of everything through our own experience.

Can we ever truly know if we are living in a simulation?

We may have no more certainty about this than if there ever was a Big Bang. However, if we are able to explain the world through the theory, it is the best possible existing hypothesis to explain what reality is. We can ourselves create complex virtual realities. Why wouldn't it be possible thus that the most massive simulation would be the reality in which we live?

If reality is a simulation, everything still works the same way as before; we don't need to invent physics all over again. Most likely, our reality is a simulation, since according to modern physics we know the world where we live is not an objective reality.

***

Hyperreality is a term presented originally by French sociologist and philosopher Jean Baudrillard, by which he described the change from face-to-face culture to the world of interfaces. Hyperreality can be seen as a condition where reality and representation collapse into each other so that there is no possibility of defining where one ends and the other begins. The physical reality mingles with virtual reality (VR) and human intelligence with artificial intelligence (AI). Hyperreality can be even more real than physical reality. Baudrillard and Umberto Eco, who has also discussed hyperreality, point to Disneyland and Las Vegas as examples of hyperreality. Hyperreality is the inability of consciousness to distinguish reality from a simulation of reality.

What if we are already living in a hyperreality, in a simulation created by consciousness?

How could we ever know that? If a simulation is our reality, we can know nothing else. If we are living in a simulation, and that doesn't necessarily change anything in our life, is it even necessary for us to know? Our reality can be a simulation, we may never know, but the most important thing is that we are able to live a good life in a reality, or a hyperreality, whether it was created by anyone or anything. This means taking into account everything we know of reality in our life.

It thus means living, taking into account everything we know of the essence of reality, of reality on all levels. We can't live the old way anymore; it is time to move on and live by taking into account everything we know from modern physics. It also means stepping forward beyond materialism, to the postmodern era. It is time for us to start *living* in hyperreality.

You may be thinking: *"What does all this really mean for me? What does this mean in my life? I have to wake up in the morning, go to school or work or other duties anyway. How could I in practice start applying the ideas of this book in my life?"*

Read the next chapter.

CHAPTER 15
LIVING IN HYPERREALITY

I am not what happened to me, I am what I choose to become.

—Carl Jung

How then should we live in hyperreality? Since the "old physics" is outdated, on what principles should we base our lives?

In this chapter I take the liberty of listening to "irrational dimensions," that is the voice of my heart, and draw together the principles of what all of the above could mean to us. I am writing these words in the first months of the year 2021. The previous year has been exceptional, totally different than what one would have expected a year ago. Since last spring, the COVID-19 disease has been spreading all over the world. However, it may be also thanks to this disease and the measures governments have taken, that many have understood that a change is needed and actually we are already living that change. This is a perfect time to stop and contemplate. What do we want to accomplish now, in this new decade? How should we live? A hundred years ago, when the 1920s began, it was described by many as an optimistic, joyous decade of reform. As a counterbalance to the First World War, to escape the reality of the war, people sought renewal through movies and literature, as well as opposition to the values of the previous century. Maybe we also understand now the need to break free from the power of materialism that ruled the previous century and search for new values? Maybe we start to live now in the way quantum mechanics has already shown us? Maybe this decade will also be seen later as a decade of peace, love, joy and change?

Principle of consciousness

Consciousness plays a significant role in reality. Consciousness seems to be the basis of everything. Many physicists and philosophers, such as

Schrödinger, Pauli, von Neumann, Wigner and Planck, have ended up proposing that consciousness is of a fundamental nature. This idea has also been a driving force during Western antiquity, and in many Eastern philosophies and mythologies. We know that consciousness and physical reality appear to be separate, but they have a connection. **Consciousness is eternal and the basis of everything**; physical reality – matter and body – is momentary. Consciousness should be elevated to its rightful place and the meaning of its fundamental role highlighted.

What does this mean then? We all have consciousness and through that we are also all connected with each other. Each one of us is a manifestation of universal consciousness. The DIH model of Bernardo Kastrup that I presented earlier in this book could well describe the birth of our consciousness. We have to change our view of who we really are. **Consider yourself, thus, primarily as a mental, spiritual, non-material being, soul, that in this life inhabits this home, and this body.** Which values rise as the most important ones with this change? We are an entity formed of matter and non-material consciousness, and our body is thus secondary. Our material, physical body is a creation and when we are born we receive our bodies as our home. Our genes and DNA won't determine our destiny, but rather we can also affect them. Our destiny is not determined and written in stone when we are born. We are an active part of reality and we affect reality, both physical and mental.

Principle of oneness

Physicist Michio Kaku articulates the principle of oneness well: "*It is impossible to completely separate ourselves from the oneness of the universe.*"

We can arrive in many ways at the conclusion that we are all one:

- The birth of our universe, the Big Bang, leads to one point, singularity, from which everything originates.
- We are all at the particle level only vibration, out of which it is impossible to distinguish what is me and what is something else. We are thus all one and the same vibration.
- Our whole reality is an information field, through which we are all connected. Information travels in this field instantaneously.

- We are all manifestations of the same universal consciousness (Kastrup's DIH model).
- Many wisdom traditions conceptualize this oneness.

We have an experience of time and distance, of separation, but experience is not the same as reality. There is no time or distance in reality; instead everything is here and now. **Learn to see that we are all of the same origin, the same oneness, energy, vibration.** The way you treat others – the way you think, act, and speak – returns back to yourself as well. In the same way, too, how you treat yourself reflects also on others, affects all those you are connected to.

Principle of interaction

We are manifestations of the same consciousness and of the same oneness and thus connected with each other. **In interaction, we give meaning to things. Interaction changes reality.** One example of this is the observer's effect in experiments; the observer affects what is observed in the experiment. Without interaction there wouldn't be any observation.

Entangled particles are also an example of interaction. We are also entangled with everyone we have ever met, in the same way as particles are entangled.

Since there is a connection between us, changes that we carry out in our own life also affect everyone else. What you put forward, including in your thoughts and feelings, also returns back to you.

It is impossible to rule out the effect of interaction, because we are always part of consciousness and reality.

Principle of complementarity

Do observer and observed actually exist? Did we somehow without knowing choose this reality, so that we could observe and learn about ourselves?

The principle of uncertainty is the core of complementarity and means that there are pairs that can't be determined accurately simultaneously, such as energy and time and location and momentum.

The universe only seems dualistic. Everything is fundamentally one, non-dualistic, but when a measurement is taken, an observation is done, the system forms as dualistic. Dualism unites as oneness again at the particle level.

We can find this kind of pair at the everyday level in such common dualities as science–religion, rich–poor, right wing–left wing, immigrants–natives, light–dark, humankind–nature, medicine–complementary therapies and so on. Even some of the most fundamental questions in our everyday life can be traced back to a confrontation that often is ultimately artificial. One example of this is the different sides of a war. Even if you obeyed the same rules, if you are on the winner's side, you are good, but if you are instead on the loser's side, you are criminal and evil. We need to learn to see what motives and factors guide our lives and learn, thus, to see deeper than opposition. It can help us rise to a whole new level. **For us to solve the world's problems, we need to see things from oneness.**

Principle of freedom

We are free to make choices; without that our life would have been decided beforehand.

The idea of statistical causality is not limited to phenomena on the particle level but is generalizable. My teacher, professor emeritus, physicist K.V. Laurikainen, even stated that the freedom linked to single events is emphasized especially in the context of life phenomena, since living organisms have the ability to adjust to the circumstances and the possibility of choices is manifested in these phenomena so clearly.

We are free to choose, within certain limits.

Instructions

The following instructions are based on the previous principles:

1. **Learn to listen to your inner talk.** Thoughts and emotions matter.
2. **Think positive thoughts about yourself and others.** We are one, and everything you do, say or think returns eventually back to you. The

outside world reflects on what I am, it is a mirror to my own inner state. The calmer I am and the more I experience feeling connected to my inner being, the more I receive similar messages from the outside world. You receive what you give. Treat yourself as you would treat any other person needing help.

3. **Remember that in reality there is no opposite or better side, because the opposites together form the whole.** When I experience being one with the environment, the framing of inner or outer, sender or receiver, observer or observed, disappears. There is only one common, all-encompassing reality. The opposition is illusory.
4. **To be able to create the future you desire, silence the conscious, thinking mind.** When you silence it, you are able to access deeper levels of creation of reality and you also free your creativity.
5. **Create your reality from love, goodness and other fundamental values.** These values have a connection to a deeper, collective level of consciousness.
6. **See your dreams in your mind as already fulfilled.** When you have created the reality in your mind, it already exists.
7. **Trust yourself, since all the information already exists in the information field.** You only need to find access to that field.
8. **Anything is possible, if you only believe it yourself.** Don't force things to happen. Instead, listen to the signs you receive and notice synchronicities.
9. **Surround yourself with those who strengthen and support you.** The power of a group is more than the sum of its parts.
10. **We have an experience of time, but neither time nor distance exists in reality.** You can thus receive information from another time, another location, even from another life or beyond the border of death.

Johanna Blomqvist

EPILOGUE

The world we live in today was imagined yesterday. The world we live in tomorrow is being imagined now.

Fundamentally, the need to understand reality originates with the desire to find one's own place in world and an answer to the question, "*Why am I here?*" Maybe we are asking the wrong questions and don't see sides of reality that we should notice, as with the heartbeats I discussed in the introduction. We think we live separately, although we are one. We consider the border of death as the end of everything, although that is not the case. We think of the visible as real, though what we don't see is even more real. We have searched for objective reality, but what we should understand is the subjective.

Perhaps more essential than answers is the asking. This book may raise more questions in the reader. Asking questions about being has changed my own relationship to life. The Being, understanding of which I am seeking, is myself. The essential point is who is asking.

Who experiences, realizes, and creates this reality is more important than knowing what all this is. I find it more important to focus on how to live this life than on why everything came into being or whether it was born at all or maybe always existed… A vision of a cartoon comes to mind, in which twins are discussing inside their mother's womb whether there is life outside the womb and the other one says: "*No, I don't believe in life after birth. When you are born, everything ends.*"

Maybe we ought not to know since we don't seem to have the means to receive information without the limitations of our observation or measurement capability? All theories about reality are only descriptions of reality, although some of them are closer to the truth than others. For example, it seems very likely that our reality is a creation of consciousness – whatever name one wishes to call it. Kastrup's DIH model and the simulation hypothesis are also interesting. With these hypotheses, it would be possible to explain those features of reality that have long been overlooked, especially the place of one's own consciousness.

Maybe we should thus focus on this moment and on the experience that we are currently having and take full advantage of this moment? Maybe we are here only because *"Earth is a wonderful place to experience and our mission is to learn from all this"* as Bashar states? Maybe we are experiencing here how change feels since in a timeless state it is impossible to experience that? Maybe when life ends we have a life review in which we go through our lives on fast-forward, as many near-death experiences tell us, and we are able to choose our next life based on this, within certain limits? Maybe our mission in this life is to let go of everything not needed so we can grow into the best version of ourselves? Maybe it is time to understand our own influence and meaning? We exist and are significant. We matter. In the same breath, I also feel that we are perfect just as we are now.

My heart tells me that the most important thing we can learn in this life is self-love and to love all others and this world.

> *Knowledge and love are thus revealed as the two cosmic forces which are apparently separate in nature but which spring from the same potency and force.*
>
> —Giordano Bruno (1548–1600)

GLOSSARY

Anecdote – from Greek word *anekdota*, which means unpublished

Axiom – assumption that is actually self-evident

Causal – according to cause and effect relation

Complementarity – a relation between two opposite states that together exhaust the possibilities; certain pairs cannot be observed or measured accurately simultaneously

Decoherence – loss of coherence; a system is coherent as long as it has particular separate quantum states

Determinism – philosophical view that all events are determined completely by previously existing causes; its opposite is indeterminism or randomness

Dualism – the belief that reality is composed of two parts, usually mind and body

Ego – conscious mind, part of identity, that is thought of as one's self

Emerge – appear, become visible

Empirical – based on experiment or observation

Genome – genetic material of an organism, includes genes and DNA

Hypothesis – proposed explanation for a phenomenon

Indeterminism – the idea that at least some events are not caused, or not caused deterministically, opposite of determinism

Intention – purpose, will to act

Invariance – unchangeability

Invariant – unchangeable

Irrational – not rational

Non-local – action at a distance; interaction may be faster than the speed of light

Observer – measurer, sometimes also experimenter, examiner (in physics observation usually means measurement)

Ontology – study of being, existence, becoming and reality

Paradigm – (Greek *paradeigma,* model example) generally accepted, established framework, theory or function of science considered correct, presented by philosopher Thomas Kuhn

Physicalism – form of ontological monism, everything is physical and there is nothing else, all forms of being we observe can be deduced back to the physical

Quantitative – based on quantities

Quantized, quantizing – to limit the possible values to a discrete set of values by quantum mechanical rules

Quantum mechanics – theory in physics that describes the properties and interactions in a microscopic level, i.e. of atoms and subatomic particles

Reductionism – philosophical viewpoint according to which a system can be reduced, i.e. a system is the sum of its parts

Sequencing – determining the nucleotide order of a given DNA fragment

Superposition – two or more quantum states can be summed up according to the superposition principle, and the end state is also a quantum state; respectively also each quantum state can presented as a sum of two or more quantum states

ACKNOWLEDGMENTS

I am grateful to my parents and to my many teachers in school, university, work and in general in life: Thank you for teaching me to question and search for answers and not to take anything for granted.

I am grateful to all my teachers also for my having learned to listen to my inner voice. If I hadn't learned to do that, this book would never have been born.

I am grateful to every one of you who have in different contexts – during my courses, lectures and other events – presented me challenging and interesting questions related to the nature of reality. All those helped me to understand the importance of writing this book. Maybe this book can provide an answer to some of those questions, or help in forming new ones.

I am grateful to the publisher of my Finnish book, Basam Books, for publishing *Hypertodellisuus*. Thank you to everyone at Basam Books and especially Batu Samaletdin for trust and support! Thank you Virpi Lehtinen, PhD for all the philosophical discussions, help in focusing and all the clarifying comments! Thanks are also due to Kosti Salminen for editing the Finnish version of the book. It was a pleasure to work with you again!

I am grateful to Tuomo Suntola, PhD and to Tarja Kallio-Tamminen, PhD for your valuable comments on the book. It was an honor to receive feedback and encouragement from you!

I am grateful to Heikki Peltola, MSc and to Asta Raami, DA. I appreciate your ability to perceive the reality, and your comments helped me to focus on the most essential issues.

I am grateful to the editor of this book, Amy Thomas, PhD. It has been a pleasure to work with you! I think the book received the final touch it needed!

I am eternally grateful to my beloved husband and soulmate Anssi. My view on reality has been substantially influenced by living over half of my life with a creative inventor such as you. Thank you for sharing this path with me! Thank you for all those conversations and everything we have and continue to ponder together! Thank you also for all those clarifying comments you made about the book!

I am grateful to our children Teo and Stella for the support and love and all those many interesting questions we have pondered together. You have helped me see so much of reality that is new!

I am grateful to all those who have supported and guided me, everywhere.

I am grateful that I was able to choose this life and mission.

REFERENCES

A.F. Ali and S. Das, "Cosmology from Quantum Potential," Physics Letters B 741, 276–279, 2015.

A.E. Allahverdyan and V. G. Gurzadyan, "Time arrow is influenced by the dark energy," Phys. Rev. E 93, 052125, 2016.

Aristotle, *Aristotle's Metaphysics*, Read Books, 2013.

Australian National University, "Experiment confirms quantum theory weirdness," ScienceDaily. ScienceDaily, 27 May 2015, https://www.sciencedaily.com/releases/2015/05/150527103110.htm.

J. Barbour, *The End of Time: The Next Revolution in Physics*, Oxford University Press, 2001.

Bashar Channeled by Darryl Anka YouTube channel.

J.S. Bell, *Speakable and Unspeakable in Quantum Mechanics*, Cambridge University Press, 1987, p. 65.

W.F. Bengston, "Commentary: a method used to train skeptical volunteers to heal in an experimental setting," J Altern and Complement Med., 13(3): 328–331, 2007.

W. Bengston, "Hands on healing: a training course in the energy cure," (CD audio set). Sounds True, 2010.

D.J. Bem, "Feeling the Future: Experimental evidence for anomalous retroactive influences on cognition and affect," Journal of Personality and Social Psychology, 100, 407–425, 2011.

H. Bergson and T.E. Hulme, *An Introduction to Metaphysics*, Hackett (September 15, 1999).

H. Bergson, transl. Arthur Mitchell, *Creative Evolution*, Henry Holt and Company, 1911.

H. Bergson, *Time and Free Will: An Essay on the Immediate Data of Consciousness*, Dover Publications, 2001.

D.J. Bierman, D.I. Radin, "Anomalous anticipatory response on randomized future conditions," Perceptual and Motor Skills 84(2), April. pp. 689–690, 1997.

D.J. Bierman, H.S. Scholte, "Anomalous anticipatory brain activation preceding exposure of emotional and neutral pictures," Proceedings of Presented Papers: The Parapsychological Association 45th Annual Convention (pp. 25–36). Cary, NC: Parapsychological Association, Inc., 2002.

P. Blasiak, Phys. Rev. A 98, 012118, 2018.

J. Blomqvist, *From Quantum Physics to Energy Healing - A Physicist's Journey to Mind and Healing*, Mindstream Publishing, 2018.

J. Blomqvist, doctoral dissertation, http://urn.fi/URN:ISBN:951-45-9929-2.

D. Bohm, *Quantum Theory*, Prentice Hall, 1951.

D. Bohm, *Wholeness and the Implicate Order*, Routledge, 1980.

D. Bohm, "A New Theory of the Relationship of Mind and Matter", Philosophical Psychology, Vol. 3, 2: 271–286, 1990.

N. Bohr, *Atomic Physics and Human Knowledge*, Wiley, 1958.

R. Boyle, *The Sceptical Chymist: or Chymico-Physical Doubts & Paradoxes*, J. Cadwell, 1661.

C.P.E. Burns, "Wolfgang Pauli, Carl Jung, and the Acausal Connecting Principle: A Case Study in Transdisciplinarity," Disciplines in Dialogue, Essay, 2011. https://www.metanexus.net/wolfgang-pauli-carl-jung-and-acausal-connecting-principle-case-study-transdisciplinarity/

F. Capra, *The Tao of Physics - An Exploration of Parallels Between Modern Physics and Eastern Mysticism*, Shambhala, 1975.

L. Carroll, *Alice's Adventures in Wonderland*, Macmillan, 1865.

D. Chalmers, *The Conscious Mind: In Search of a Fundamental Theory*, Oxford University Press, 1996.

D. Chopra, M. Kafatos, *You Are the Universe: Discovering Your Cosmic Self and Why It Matters*, Random House, 2017.

D. Chopra, R. Penrose, H. Stapp, B. Carter *et al.*, *How Consciousness Became the Universe: Quantum Physics, Cosmology, Neuroscience, Parallel Universes*, Cosmology Science, 2015, 2016.

D. Chopra, "Reality and consciousness: A view from the East: Comment on Consciousness in the universe: A review of the 'Orch OR' theory" by Stuart Hameroff and Roger Penrose," Physics of Life Reviews, Vol. 11, Issue 1, 81–82, 2014.

P.C.W. Davies and J.R. Brown, *The Ghost in the Atom: A Discussion of the Mysteries of Quantum Physics*, 1986/1993, pp. 45–46.

R. Descartes, *Meditations on First Philosophy*, (Latin: Meditationes de Prima Philosophia, in qua Dei existentia et animæ immortalitas demonstratur, 1641), French translation, 1647 as Méditations Métaphysiques.

R. Descartes, "The Search for Truth by the Light of Nature" (Adam, Charles; Tannery, Paul, eds. (1901), "La Recherche de la Vérité par La Lumiere Naturale," *Oeuvres de Descartes*, X, p. 535).

B.S. DeWitt, "Quantum Theory of Gravity. I. The Canonical Theory," Phys. Rev. 160 (5): 1113–1148, 1967.

B. Dunne, R. Jahn, *Being & Biology - Is Consciousness the Life Force?*, ICRL Press, 2017.

F. J. Dyson, "The Radiation Theories of Tomonaga, Schwinger, and Feynman," Phys. Rev. 75, 486, 1949.

J.C. Eccles, *Facing Reality - Philosophical Adventures by a Brain Scientist*, Springer-Verlag Berlin Heidelberg, 1970.

J.C. Eccles, *How the Self Controls Its Brain*, Berlin: Springer-Verlag, 1994.

Sir A. Eddington, *Science and the Unseen World*, Macmillan, 1929.

The Feynman Lectures on Physics, https://www.feynmanlectures.caltech.edu/info/

A. Freeman (ed.), *Consciousness and its Place in Nature. Does Physicalism Entail Panpsychism?* Galen Strawson *et al.* Exeter: Imprint Academic, 2006.

G. Galilei, *Collected Works of Galileo Galilei (Illustrated)*, Delphi Classics, 2017.

G. Galilei, *The Assayer*, 1623.

Global Consciousness Project: http://noosphere.princeton.edu/results.html

G. Gamow, *Thirty Years That Shook Physics – The Story of Quantum Theory*, 1966.

S. Gieser, *The Innermost Kernel: Depth Psychology and Quantum Physics: Wolfgang Pauli's Dialogue with C.G. Jung*, Springer, 2005.

A. Goswami, *The Everything Answer Book: How Quantum Science Explains Love, Death, and the Meaning of Life*, Hampton Roads, 2017.

A. Gregory, *Harvey's Heart: The Discovery of Blood Circulation*, Icon Books, 2001.

J. Grinberg-Zylberbaum, M. Delaflor, L. Attie, A. Goswami, "The Einstein-Podolsky-Rosen Paradox in the Brain: The Transferred Potential," Physics Essays, Vol. 7: Pages 422–428, 1994.

J. Grinberg-Zylberbaum, "Patterns of Interhemispheric Correlation During Human Communication," International Journal of Neuroscience. 36 (1–2): 41–53, 1987.

J. Hagelin, *et al.* "Effects of Group Practice of the Transcendental Meditation Program on Preventing Violent Crime in Washington, D.C.," Social Indicators Research, 47(2), June, 153–201, 1999.

J. Hagelin. "Is Consciousness the Unified Field? A Field Theorist's Perspective," Modern Science and Vedic Science, 1, 29–87,1987.

J. Hagelin. "Veda and Physics: The Science and Technology of the Unified Field," https://www.youtube.com/watch?v=4u3f7_p1i8c

B. Haisch, *The God Theory: Universes, Zero-point Fields, And What's Behind It All*, Red Wheel/Weiser Books, 2006.

B. Haisch, SSE Channel, "Is the Universe a Consciousness-created VR-simulation?" https://youtu.be/xOBv5UST6P8

S. Hameroff, R. Penrose, "Consciousness in the Universe: A review of the 'Orch OR' theory," Physics of Life Reviews, Vol. 11, Issue 1, 39–78, 2014.

S. Hameroff, R. Penrose, "Reply to Seven Commentaries on Consciousness in the Universe: Review of the 'Orch OR' theory," Physics of Life Reviews, Vol. 11, Issue 1, 94–100, 2014.

W. Heisenberg, *Physics and Beyond*, Harper & Row, 1971.

W. Heisenberg, *Physics and Philosophy*, Harper & Row, 1958.

R. C. Henry, "The Mental Universe," Nature 436: 29, 2005.

B.J. Hiley, P. Pylkkänen, "Can mind affect matter via active information," Mind & Matter Vol. 3(2), pp. 7–27, Imprint Academic, 2005.

T. Hobbes, *Leviathan or The Matter, Forme and Power of a Common Wealth Ecclesiasticall and Civil, commonly called Leviathan*, 1651.

D. Hoffman, *The Case against Reality: Why Evolution Hid the Truth from Our Eyes*, Norton, 2019.

E. Husserl, *Ideas Pertaining to a Pure Phenomenology and to a Phenomenological Philosophy – Third Book: Phenomenology and the Foundations of the Sciences*, trans. Klein, T. E., and Pohl, W. E., Kluwer, 1980.

H.J. Irwin, C. Watt, *An Introduction to Parapsychology*, 5th Revised edn, McFarland, 2007.

Jackdaws: https://yle.fi/uutiset/3-9245545

R. Jahn, B. Dunne, "The Uses and Misuses of Quantum Jargon," April–June, Number 7, EdgeScience, 2011.

C.G. Jung, "Synchronicity: An Acausal Connecting Principle," Bollingen Foundation (From Vol. 8. of the Collected Works of C. G. Jung), 1952, 1993.

M. Kaku, R. O'Keefe, *Hyperspace: A Scientific Odyssey Through Parallel Universes, Time Warps, and the Tenth Dimension*, Oxford University Press, 1994.

M. Kaku, *Parallel Worlds: A Journey Through Creation, Higher Dimensions, and the Future of the Cosmos*, Doubleday, 2004.

T. Kallio-Tamminen, *Kvanttilainen todellisuus - Fysiikka ja filosofia maailmankuvan muovaajina*, Gaudeamus, 2012 (book available only in Finnish).

T. Kaluza, *Zum Unitätsproblem in der Physik*. Sitzungsber. Preuss. Akad. Wiss., https://archive.org/details/sitzungsberichte1921preussi, 1921.

T. Kassila, *Meeting with the Masters*, Om-kustannus, 2021.

B. Kastrup, *Dreamed Up Reality: Diving into the Mind to Uncover the Astonishing Hidden Tale of Nature*, John Hunt, 2011.

B. Kastrup, *Why Materialism Is Baloney: How True Sceptics Know There Is No Death and Fathom Answers to Life, the Universe and Everything*, John Hunt, 2014.

B. Kastrup, *The Idea of the World, A Multidisciplinary Argument for the Mental Nature of Reality*, John Hunt, 2019.

B. Kastrup, *Analytic Idealism: A Consciousness-Only Ontology*, Dissertation, Radboud University Nijmegen, 2019.

S. Kauffman, *Humanity in a Creative Universe*, Oxford University Press, 2016.

J. Kaufman, *The World Around Us*, Western Publ., 1978 (In Finnish: Tällainen on maailma, Tammi, 1979).

E.F. Kelly, A. Crabtree and P. Marshall, *Beyond Physicalism: Toward Reconciliation of Science and Spirituality*, Rowman & Littlefield, 2015.

E.F. Kelly, E.W. Kelly, *Irreducible Mind: Toward a Psychology for the 21st Century*, Rowman & Littlefield, 2009.

O. Klein, "Quantentheorie und fünfdimensionale Relativitätstheorie," Zeitschrift für Physik A. 37 (12): 895–906, 1926.

C. Koch, *The Feeling of Life Itself: Why Consciousness Is Widespread but Can't Be Computed*, The MIT Press, 2019.

R.C. Koons, *The Waning of Materialism*, Oxford University Press, 2010.

M. Kuhlmann, "Physicists Debate Whether the World Is Made of Particles or Fields – or Something Else Entirely," Scientific American, August, 2013 pp. 40.

T. Kuhn, *The Structure of Scientific Revolutions*. University of Chicago Press, 1962.

K.V. Laurikainen, dissertation (in Finnish): "Tieteellä on rajansa: Kvanttiteoria ja todellisuus," Yliopistopaino, 1997.

R. Letzter, "Something Strange Punched a Hole in the Milky Way. But What Exactly Is It," Live Science: https://www.livescience.com/65483-dark-impactor-could-be-dark-matter.html

B. Libet, E.W. Wright Jr., B. Feinstein, D.K. Pearl, Dennis K, "Subjective Referral of the Timing for a Conscious Sensory Experience – A Functional Role for the Somatosensory Specific Projection System in Man," Brain, 102: 193–224, 1979.

B. Libet, A. Freeman, and J. K. B. Sutherland, (eds), *The Volitional Brain: Towards a Neuroscience of Free Will*, Imprint Academic, 1999.

B. Libet, "Reflections on the Interaction of the Mind and Brain," Progress in Neurobiology, 78 (3–5): 322–326, 2006.

V. LoBue, J.S. DeLoache, "Detecting the snake in the grass: Attention to fear-relevant stimuli by adults and young children," Psychol Sci., 19(3): 284–289, 2008.

W. von Lucadou, H. Römer and H. Walach, "Synchronistic Phenomena as Entanglement Correlations in Generalized Quantum Theory," Journal of Consciousness Studies 14(4): 50–74, 2007.

L. McTaggart, *The Field: The Quest for the Secret Force of the Universe,* Free Press, 2003.

L. McTaggart *The Power of Eight: The Power of Eight: Harnessing the Miraculous Energies of a Small Group to Heal Others, Your Life, and the World,* Atria Books, 2018.

L. McTaggart, *The Intention Experiment: Using Your Thoughts to Change Your Life and the World,* Free Press, 2007.

N.D. Mermin, "Hidden Variables and the Two Theorems of John Bell," Reviews of Modern Physics. 65 (3): 803–815, 1993.

F.A. Mesmer, Dissertatio physico-medica de planetarum influxu ("Physical-medical dissertation on planetary influence"). Vindobonae (Wien) Ghelen, 1766.

J. Mishlove, *The PK Man: A True Story of Mind Over Matter,* Hampton Roads, 2000.

B. Misra, E.C.G. Sudarshan, "The Zeno's Paradox in Quantum Theory," J. Math Phys. 18(4) 756, 1977.

Monkey dancing: https://youtu.be/vJG698U2Mvo

W. Moore, *A Life of Erwin Schrodinger,* Cambridge University Press, Canto reprint, 1994.

E. Moreva, G. Brida, M. Gramegna, V. Giovannetti, L. Maccone, M. Genovese, "Time from quantum entanglement: An experimental illustration," Phys Rev. A89, 052122, 2014.

J. Mossbridge, T. Cheung, *The Premonition Code: The Science of Precognition, How Sensing the Future Can Change Your Life,* Watkins, 2018.

R. Nadeau, M. Kafatos, *The Non-Local Universe: The New Physics and Matters of the Mind,* Oxford University Press, 2001.

T. Nagel, *Mind and Cosmos: Why the Materialist Neo-Darwinian Conception of Nature is Almost Certainly False,* Oxford University Press, 2012.

J. von Neumann, *Mathematical Foundations of Quantum Mechanics,* Princeton University Press, 1932, revised 1955.

I. Newton, *Philosophiae Naturalis Principia Mathematica,* alkuperäinen 1687, The Project Gutenberg Ebook, 2009.

G. Nordström, Gunnar, "Über die Möglichkeit, das elektromagnetische Feld und das Gravitationsfeld zu vereinigen," Physikalische Zeitschrift. 15: 504–506, 1914.

D.N. Page and W.K. Wootters, "Evolution without Evolution: Dynamics Described by Stationary Observables," Phys. Rev. D 27, 2885, 1983.

Paramahansa Yogananda, *Autobiography of a Yogi*, Rider, 1955.

W. Pauli, "Modern Examples of Background Physics" ("Moderne Beispiele zur Hintergrundsphysik," 1948) trans. David Roscoe in *Atom and Archetype*, 1992.

H. Peltola, *Whole and One – Seeing and Being the World*, Basam Books, 2020, https://www.heikkipeltola.com/en/whole-and-one/.

Planaria articles: http://www.drmichaellevin.org/refs_planaria.html

Plato, *Timaues*, Trans. B. Jowett / Subtitles added by Elpenor (https://www.ellopos.net/elpenor/physis/plato-timaeus/default.asp)

PEAR project:

- R.G. Jahn, B.J. Dunne, "A modular model of mind/matter manifestations (M5)," J. Scientific Exploration, 15: 299–329, 2001.
- R.G. Jahn, B.J. Dunne, "The PEAR Proposition," Journal of Scientific Exploration, 19 (2) pp. 195–246, 2005.
- R.G. Jahn, B.J. Dunne, *Margins of Reality: The Role of Consciousness in the Physical World*, ICRL Press, p. 203, originally published by Harcourt Brace Jovanovich in 1987, 2009.
- R.G. Jahn, B.J. Dunne, *Consciousness and the Source of Realty: The PEAR Odyssey*, ICRL Press, 2011.
- R.G. Jahn, B.J. Dunne, R.D. Nelson, Y.H. Dobyns and G.J. Bradish, "Correlations of Random Binary Sequences with Pre-Stated Operator Intention: A Review of a 12-Year Program," J. Scientific Exploration, 11, No. 3, pp. 345–367, 1997.

D. Podolsky, R. Lanza, "On Decoherence in quantum gravity," Annalen der Physik, 528, 9–10, 663–676, 2016.

J.B. Priestley, *Man and Time*, Aldus Books, 1964.

P. Pylkkänen, *Mind, Matter and Implicate Order*, Springer Verlag, 2007.

Quantum Zeno effect: https://phys.org/news/2015-10-zeno-effect-verifiedatoms-wont.html#jCp

D.I. Radin, L. Michel, P. Wendland, R. Rickenbach, A. Delorme, K. Galdamez, "Consciousness and the double-slit interference pattern: Six experiments," Physics Essays, 25 (2), 157–171, 2012.

D.I. Radin, A. Delorme, L. Michel, J. Johnston, "Psychophysical interactions with a double-slit interference pattern: Experiments and a model," Physics Essays. 26 (4), 553–566, 2013.

D. Radin, *Entangled Minds: Extrasensory Experiences in a Quantum Reality,* Paraview Pocket Books, 2006.

D. Radin, N. Lundgren, M. Emoto, T. Kizu, "Effects of Distant Intention on Water Crystal Formation: A Triple-Blind Replication," Journal of Scientific Exploration, 2008.

K.L. Reichenbach, "Researches on Magnetism, Electricity, Heat and Light in their Relations to Vital Forces," Annalen der Chemie und Physik", Vol. 105, 9, 62–64, 1833.

J.B. Rhine, Rhine, J.G. Pratt, *Parapsychology: "Frontier Science of the Mind"*, Charles C. Thomas, 1957.

C. Rovelli, *Reality Is Not What It Seems: The Journey to Quantum Gravity,* Penguin Random House, 2016.

C. Rovelli and L. Smolin, "Loop space representation of quantum general relativity," Nucl. Phys. B 331 80, 1990.

C. Rovelli, *Loop Quantum Gravity,* CERN, 2008.

B. Russell, *Unpopular Essays,* Simon and Schuster, 1950.

E. Schrödinger, Naturwissenschaften 23, 807 (1935).

E. Schrödinger, *What Is Life? The Physical Aspect of the Living Cell with Mind and Matter,* Cambridge University Press, 1944.

G. Schwartz, *Super Synchronicity: Where Science and Spirit Meet,* Waterfront Digital Press, 2017.

R. Sheldrake, *A New Science of Life (UK) / Morphic Resonance (US),* 1988, Revised version 2009.

R. Sheldrake, *Dogs That Know When Their Owners Are Coming Home: And Other Unexplained Powers of Animals,* Arrow, 2000.

Morphic fields and implicate order, Sheldrake discusses with Bohm: https://www.sheldrake.org/files/pdfs/A_New_Science_of_Life_Appx_B.pdf

W. de Sitter, "On Einstein's Theory of Gravitation and Its Astronomical Consequences. Third Paper," Monthly Notices of the Royal Astronomical Society, papers 1–3, 2016–2017.

D. Skrbina, *Panpsychism in the West,* The MIT Press, 2005.

J. P. Spottiswoode and E.C. May, "Skin Conductance Prestimulus Response: Analyses, Artifacts and a Pilot Study," Journal of Scientific Exploration, Vol. 17, No. 4, pp. 617–641, 2003.

H. Stapp, *Mind, Matter and Quantum Mechanics,* Springer, 1993.

H. Strasburger, B. Waldvogel, "Sight and blindness in the same person: Gating in the visual system," Psych Journal, 2015.

T. Suntola, *The Dynamic Universe – Towards a Unified Picture of Physical Reality*, Physics Foundations Society, 2018.

E. Swedenborg, trans. G.F. Dole, *Heaven and Hell: New Century Edition*, Swedenborg Foundation, 2010, (orig. 1758).

E. Swedenborg, *Scribe of Heaven, Swedenborg's Life, Work, and Impact*, edd J.S. Rose, S. Shotwell, and M.L. Bertucci, Swedenborg Foundation, 2005.

C.T. Tart, *The End of Materialism: How Evidence of the Paranormal is Bringing Science and Spirit Together*, New Harbinger Publications, 2009.

J.M.E. Taggart, "The Unreality of Time," Mind, 17: 457–473, 1908.

R. Targ, *The Reality of ESP, A Physicist's Proof of Psychic Abilities*, Quest Books, 2012.

R. Targ, "What Do We Know about Psi? The First Decade of Remote-Viewing Research and Operations at Stanford Research Institute," JSE Vol. 33, No. 4, pp. 569–592, 2019.

T. Toivonen, *Vapauden Illuusio. Henkinen kasvu tietoteknisen kehityksen tasapainottajana*, Rasalas Kustannus, 2001 (available only in Finnish).

G. Tononi, *Phi: A Voyage from the Brain to the Soul*, Pantheon, 2012.

S. Uchii, "Leibniz's Theory of Time," (presentation) DLMPS Helsinki, 2015.

A. Vannini and U. Di Corpo, *Retrocausality: Experiments and Theory*, Independently published, 2016.

M. Velmans, *Consciousness* (Critical Concepts in Psychology) Major Works Series, 4 Volumes, Routledge, 2018.

M. Velmans, *Understanding Consciousness*, Routledge, 2000.

A. Vesalius, *The Fabric of the Human Body. An Annotated Translation of the 1543 and 1555 Editions*, ed. D.H. Garrison and M.H. Hast, Northwestern University, 2003.

H. Walach, N. von Stillfried, "Generalised Quantum Theory – Basic Idea and General Intuition: A Background Story and Overview," Axiomathes, 21:185–209, 2011.

E. Wargo, *Time Loops: Precognition, Retrocausation, and Unconscious*, Anomalist Books, 2018.

J. A. Wheeler, K.W. Ford, *Geons, Black Holes & Quantum Foam: A Life in Physics*, Norton; Revised ed., 2000.

B. Whitworth, "The Physical World as a Virtual Reality", http://www.cs.auckland.ac.nz/staff-cgi-bin/mjd/secondcgi.pl?serial, 2008.

F. Wilczek, *The Lightness of Being: Mass, Ether, and the Unification of Forces*, Basic Books, 2009.

A.M. Young, *The Reflexive Universe – Evolution of Consciousness*, Anodos Foundation, 1999.

ABOUT THE BOOK AND AUTHOR

How should we approach life and its challenges? Are they real?

What do we really know about reality?

What is the connection between reality and consciousness?

Do we live in a simulation?

Hyperreality is a book about the nature of our reality and the hypotheses we have made about it through the centuries. Johanna Blomqvist, PhD describes many cases and research experiments that will puzzle your mind. Our reality seems to be something other than what the current prevailing model which guides our life suggests.

It is time to understand our effect on physical reality and move to a new era, beyond materialism. You exist – dive into hyperreality, in which you are a significant participant!

Johanna Blomqvist, PhD is a physicist, entrepreneur and internationally published author. In her work, she combines a wide variety of fields and methods in a unique way, often discussing topics from the cutting edge and unconventional areas of science. Blomqvist is a sought-after lecturer and trainer.

www.johannablomqvist.com

Printed in Great Britain
by Amazon